Praise for

"*Math Recess* is a call for disruption—a "do-over" in playground language—of the way we structure the teaching of mathematics. So much of mathematics is navigating relationships and deciding what really matters—skills honed in play...at recess. Learning is meant to be an experience, and this book is a reminder that math is a very human endeavor and we are all part of telling its story. Return math class to the students, and let them play!"

—**Dee Crescitelli, EdD,** director of Kentucky Center of Mathematics

"*Math Recess* burns the broken math education system to the ground and re-imagines it with sheer joy and playfulness. This book will revive your inner child, challenge you with messy math, and inspire you to lend your voice to the chorus of diverse thought needed to resuscitate math education. Double-knot your shoelaces and get ready for an epic recess!"

—**Berkeley Everett,** K–5 math coach, facilitator for UCLA Math Project

"'*Ding dong*! The witch is dead! Which old witch?'

"In *Math Recess*, Sunil Singh and Dr. Christopher S. Brownell drop a house upon the idea that Math is best done through solitary tedium. Both authors give us an alternative path to teach this beautiful subject... one that is full of joyful play. Equal parts 'how to' and EDU philosophy, this is a must-read for lovers and haters of math."

—**Stepan Pruchnicky,** experiential learning lead, Toronto Catholic District School Board

"*Math Recess* is a book that urges reader participation. As I found myself tinkering my way through the many math puzzles contained in the book, I was pleasantly reminded not only that math is a social activity, but that math allows us to find happiness. *Math Recess* is a treasure trove that needs to be read, and shared, by anyone who teaches math."

—**Michael Jacobs,** president, Ontario Math Coordinators Association

"To read *Math Recess* by Dr. Chris Brownell and Sunil Singh is to take a magical journey that transcends the typical boundaries of a book about mathematics.

—**Dr. Sue Looney,** consultant, author of *Ying and the Magic Turtle*

"*Math Recess: Playful Learning for an Age of Disruption* will inspire you to rekindle genuine excitement and passion for mathematics. Sunil Singh and Dr. Christopher S. Brownell take readers on a journey to reimagine the spirit of math through relatable stories, research, and examples. Serving as a roadmap for transforming teaching and learning, this is a book you'll reach for often as you disrupt the perception of mathematics by infusing play and sparking creative thought.

—**Elisabeth Bostwick,** instructional coach, speaker, author of *Take the L.E.A.P.*

"Sunil and Chris take you on a wild ride through mathematics that will engage you in the same manner that mathematics should be instructed. Stereotypical barriers have been broken with their ideas so that you will never think of math the same way. Whether you are an educator, parent, mathematician, or just a free thinker, *Math Recess* will provide you with amazing practical and philosophical ideas."

—**Dr. Matthew Beyranevand,** author, creator of *Math with Matthew*

"Sunil Singh's first book, *Pi of Life*, was an endearing love letter to mathematics. In his second book, Sunil Singh joins with Dr. Christopher S. Brownell to ask why we can't all fall in love with the beauty of mathematics, and they ambitiously provide a roadmap of how to discover that love in *Math Recess*.

—**Erica Heinzman,** lecturer/supervisor, secondary education, University of California, San Diego

Math Recess beautifully encapsulates the gaps in current mathematics curriculum, and blesses teachers with the courage and confidence to go back to a blank slate and to redesign their mathematical teachings. The resources shared, with links and pictures, add to the pleasure and ease of reading this book. I absolutely loved this book from start to finish, and was saddened, as I was as a child, that recess is so short."

—**Evelin Niemiec,** math coach, Hamilton, Ontario

"This book shouts, "Let them play math!" An insightful journey into the human connection of playing and learning. With facts, humor, and heart, Sunil and Chris raise a battle cry for change.

—**Sophia Stier,** creator of LilMathGirl

"So freaking *great*! *Math Recess* provides a clear insight into the purpose of education as a human endeavor that should include joy and play, which culminates as socialization. Chris and Sunil's storytelling and experiences breathe life into the learning of mathematics. As a math coach, I cannot wait to lead a book study around this book with all of my middle and high school teachers.

—**Cassie Sisemore,** math coach, secondary mathematics, Visalia Unified School District

"*Math Recess* spoke to three areas of my life: math coach, administrator, and grandparent. We need to inspire our students and families to live in a math playground where every day there is learning that is not only relevant but fun!

—**Laurie Duerksen,** teacher on special assignment, secondary curriculum, Valley Oak Middle School

This book is a lovingly curated unapologetic selection of heart-warming, hair-pulling, joy-eliciting mathematics and para-mathematical stories that asks us all to consider the most fundamental and transformative question for mathematics education, 'What if we ...?'

"This is a hopeful invitation to everyone, but especially those hurt by school mathematics, to come play—you are welcome, you belong. Grab a pencil, tablet, phone, some friends, and prepare to play hard! Have bandages handy—there will be scrapes and bruises. Pure *funstration*!"

—**Steve Khan, PhD, MEd, BSc,** assistant professor, Elementary Education, University of Alberta

"Confusing? Yes. Action packed? Definitely. Riddled with plot twists? Absolutely. Mysterious? Totally. Hilarious? Positively. Romantic? Of course. Sad? At times. Terrifying? Actually, yes, quite! One of the most important educational works of the past decade? Easily. A blockbuster of a book, *Math Recess* dares us to finally get off of our mathematically oppressed couches, grab the remote, and fundamentally change the channel!"

—**Vanessa Vakharia,** founder, the Math Guru;
author, *Math Hacks*; rockstar (Goodnight, Sunrise)

"Sunil and Chris have given maths punks like myself nothing short of a call to arms! *Math Recess* is not only a fun read, it's a veritable toy box for math classes of all ages. THIS is what maths class should look like! For those about to disrupt, we salute you!"

—**Michael Wilkinson,** STEAM educator, curriculum designer,
Fieldston Lower School, Bronx, New York

"*Math Recess* gives educators PD recess in the form of a thoroughly satisfying book. I laughed, I cried, and I wrestled with my own understandings. All the things Singh and Brownell encourage us to do with students in the classroom, they have us doing in this book—from beginning to end!"

—**Christina Tondevold,** recovering traditionalist;
facilitator, Build Math Minds

Math Recess will be one of my go-to resources for presenting what *doing* math can look and feel like—challenging, fun and extremely rewarding. I would recommend the book to anyone who wants to experience the joy of math."

—**Amrit Sharma,** Connected Mathematics Project,
Michigan State University

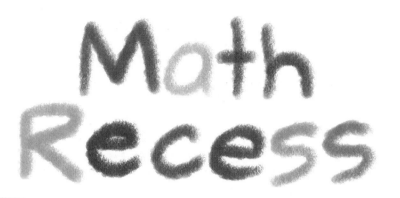

Math Recess

Playful Learning
in an Age
of Disruption

**Sunil Singh and
Dr. Christopher Brownell**
Foreword by Dan Finkel

Math Recess

©2019 by Sunil Singh and Dr. Christopher Brownell

This book is available at special discounts when purchased in quantity for use as premiums, promotions, fundraisers, or for educational use. For inquiries and details, contact the publisher at books@impressbooks.org.

The author has tried to recreate certain events, locales, and conversations from his memory. Names, physical characteristics, and identifying details have been altered to protect the privacy of individuals. Some sections of this book include names, characters, places, and events that are part of the author's imagination. In these instances, any resemblance to actual persons or events is purely coincidental.

Published by IMPress, a division of Dave Burgess Consulting, Inc.
ImpressBooks.org
daveburgessconsulting.com
Editing and Interior Design by My Writers' Connection
Cover Design by Genesis Kohler

Library of Congress Control Number: 2019936980
Paperback ISBN: 978-1-948334-10-5
eBook ISBN: 978-1-948334-11-2
First Printing: April 2019

Dedication

We'd both like to dedicate this book to teachers of mathematics everywhere. You inspire minds, invigorate discussions, and create playful and joyful learning situations. Furthermore, to you parents who turn the mundane moments of your day with your children into mind experiments and opportunities to play with ideas, we dedicate this work with the hope that you might find fuel for your conversations. Finally, to all of you who enjoy gathering with others to share a meal, a round of good ale, or simply an afternoon at the beach with good company: this book and its contents are for you as well.

Ding, ding! The bell has rung; it is time for RECESS!

Contents

Foreword

BY DAN FINKEL

Math education is in an era of upheaval.

Computers can solve, instantly and perfectly, any exercise in a typical K–12 math curriculum. A far-reaching, fertile, and, at times, fractious conversation is underway about what the goals of teaching mathematics should be, and how best to get there. Should we be trying to teach problem-solving or help kids memorize facts? (Or do you need facts in order to problem-solve?) Do students need to explain their answers, or is it enough to get the answer right? Or, because they can do a Google search for all the answers anyway, does the fundamental structure of the classroom need to change?

While I'm interested in and sympathetic to many points of view, there are, for me, a few nonnegotiables.

The first of these is the recognition that our system of education has not, and has never, worked reliably well to teach the majority of students math. While some have excelled, there are generations of mathematically traumatized people in our world. I meet them on a regular basis, and their pain is real. People literally give up their dreams—of being, say, an architect, a doctor, a nurse, a veterinarian—because there's a math test or math course in their way. I've seen adults moved to tears as they retell the humiliations and failures of math classes from their childhood. Any solution that doesn't acknowledge and address this is direly incomplete.

My second nonnegotiable is a belief that mathematics is for everyone. Which is to say, mathematical thinking about number, shape, structure, pattern, and the basic numerical literacy required to participate productively in today's society is within everyone's grasp. The ability to make sense of the world and its underlying order is our biological inheritance as human beings, and mathematical thinking is simply this sense-making ability refined and supercharged. If our solutions are about finding the "math people," you'll find me a skeptic.

Third, any solution to what mathematical teaching and learning should look like needs to include playing around with real, honest-to-god mathematics. If we're afraid to participate in the process of thinking about math, we're in trouble before we begin.

Whether you're new to this conversation or a seasoned veteran, you're beginning a book by two of its most ardent participants, and the arguments, examples, and inspiration from these pages should help guide how the questions of this era of disruption in mathematics teaching are resolved. Sunil Singh and Chris Brownell go beyond the nonnegotiables above, giving us a full-throated defense of a mathematics built on play and a love of learning. And if that doesn't sound like the mathematics you remember from school, well, maybe the problem was with your school.

The fact that we have, in the United States and many other countries, public systems devoted to educating everyone, for free, is miraculous. Still, systems have a way of hardening, until the humans inside them are trapped in strange positions and behaviors. The promise of disruption is that those systems will soften or break, the futile and meaningless parts of them will be jettisoned, and the parts that support human flourishing will stay. How change flows through systems is a problem that will not be solved quickly, or by any single book or person. As we imagine what mathematics education can and should look like, the arguments in this book and its portraits of playful, joyful, challenging and meaningful mathematics should inspire us to look beyond test scores, beyond senseless exercises, and beyond the way it was when we were kids. Singh and Brownell's vision of mathematics education stokes our imagination of the possible, without the compromises, driven by creativity and play and joy, built to enable our fundamental humanity as we practice it.

What should mathematics education look like? You can make your own judgment. But before you do, spend some time on the mathematical playground with Singh and Brownell.

The Sweet Sound of Disruption

"... And two subtract one is one. I win again. Next!"

Asking for student volunteers in a math class usually produced an edgy, nervous silence. Not that day. On that day, a standard high school recursion formula, disguised as an accessible game, elicited the most atypical response—chaotic happiness on a second-floor room in an elementary school.

In Michael Wilkinson's fourth-grade class at Fieldston Lower School in the Bronx, everyone's hand was up in the air. Some students were supporting one of their flailing arms with the other one. Anything to be the next contestant in the mathematically perplexing Fifty Game.

Channeling some goofy amalgam of Bob Barker and Sideshow Bob from *The Simpsons*, I (Sunil) surveyed the classroom for a clever hero who could vanquish the losses of the previous five students.

I called upon Lucius "Sushi Roulette" LoCicero—a personality even bigger than his awesome name.

Before I started my math games with the class, I wanted to know everyone's name and favorite food. Lucius' response was, naturally, head-shakingly amazing. His favorite food was "Sushi Roulette." This got the required supportive laughter not only from the class but from me as well. So much so, I immediately walked over to Lucius, pulled up a seat, sat down, and asked, "What the hell is sushi roulette?" Laughing hysterically as well, Lucius said it was sushi with one of the rolls loaded with wasabi. I told him that was the most awesome thing I had heard in a while. Before heading back to the front to resume my game show host duties, I gave Lucius a much-deserved fist bump.

> ### *The real 1:1 is about making personal connections with every one of your students and less about the number of technological devices that should be your classroom has.*
>
> —**Brian Aspinall**, educator and author
> of *Code Breaker* and *Block Breaker*

As with the other students before him, Lucius looked back at the "audience" for help deciding which number to subtract. Like the frenzied audience on *The Price is Right,* everyone thought they had the winning move. All the students laughed and yelled, and Sushi Roulette felt like the star of the show. Awash in goofy math bliss, the whole room sounded like *recess.*

Introduction

*All too often the rabbit hole is
as far as you have dug.*

—Gary Hopkins

The date was October 6, 2017—one of the most auspicious days in the evolution of the book you are holding. The morning was a joyful, carefree, and happy romp through a bouillabaisse of math puzzles, problems, and perplexities in the Bronx. The afternoon had me (Sunil) shuttle off to a tiny cafe in Brooklyn to meet the most important person in shaping my views on math education over the past twenty years. How important? Imagine being a beer league hockey player or scratch golfer and getting invited to lunch by Bobby Orr or Annika Sörenstam in their hometown. This person was *that* important.

After arriving at Tazza café several minutes before our 1:30 meeting, I pulled out a hardcover copy of my first book, *Pi of Life: The Hidden Happiness of Mathematics*, glanced over the signed page, and slid it to the opposite side of the small table I had secured.

Then I sat back and waited. Before long, 1:30 came and went. As did 1:31, 1:32, and 1:33. That's how nervous I was. By 1:40, my gut feeling was that something had gone wrong. *Gone wrong on my side.*

My lunch companion had emailed me that he would have to leave by 2:30 at the latest. I walked to the counter and asked the question that I dreaded hearing the answer to: "Is there another Tazza café?" The person, sensing my deflating tone, replied with an almost embarrassed, "Yes." Another location was *just* a fifteen-minute walk up the street. I didn't think I had one more minute, let alone fifteen, but I quickly shuffled out of Tazza One to head to Tazza Two. Faster than a speed-walk but slower than a mangled sprint, I huffed and puffed my way into the correct meeting place. The time was 1:58. I was a perfect twenty-eight minutes late (I would have preferred six!). But he was there. Wearing the green shirt and black shorts he described in his email, Paul Lockhart sat unassumingly in the corner, flipping through a signed copy of his third book, *Arithmetic*.

Eight years after we started communicating—just before he published his landmark first book, *A Mathematician's Lament: How School Cheats Us out of Our Most Fascinating and Imaginative Art Form*—we were finally about to meet. Our initial conversations swirled around many of the elements that are contained in that book. And, like good wine I suppose, they are uncorked a decade later!

Paul Lockhart <plockhart@saintannsny.org>
Thu 2/19/2009, 8:52 PM
You ⩔

Dear Sunil,

I'm sorry to be so slow in responding. I have been getting A Mathematician's Lament
(the book version) ready for publication, and it has taken forever. It's coming out
in April.

I took a look at the material you sent me. Obviously we see eye to eye on the state of math education, and no amount of complaining and excoriation of the forces at work can possibly be enough. So I'm glad that you are pursuing this project. Your choices of targets and the points you are making are absolutely dead on and very timely and important.

Never in my wildest dreams had I ever expected that we might one day exchange signed books. The previous anxiety-riddled moments evaporated with our earnest embrace, and the hour that followed was like being at the Oracle of Delphi with Willy Wonka—deep wisdom soaked with charming quirkiness. In that all-too-brief meeting, I was lucky to snatch a gold nugget from Lockhart. As we said our good-byes, he nonchalantly remarked, "*My job is to provide math recess.*"

Mic drop.

In the seconds after Lockhart shared those two seemingly disjointed words, I knew that I had to write a second book and that the title had to be *Math Recess*. At that same moment, I decided the purpose of the book, at its heart, would be to transform the oil-and-water relationship between *math* and *recess* into something more like bread and butter. (Sorry, but as delicious as it sounds, I have never had peaches and cream.)

One of the key ideas about recess is socialization and nurturing friendships. It only made complete sense to deeply write about mathematical play with my good friend Chris Brownell. We make a good team because we agree that our mission isn't to build a bridge between recess and math. That bridge already exists. Construction started, oh, a few thousand years ago. Our mission is to create a more delectable way of discovering mathematics—one that is bold and boisterous! Taking the same care that we use when folding in egg whites, we want to fold math into our students' social and experiential learning.

A Siren's Call

I (Chris) think most people would agree that recess is the epitome of childhood freedom and delight, while doing math is on par with detention or being sent to the principal's office. Sunil and I want to change that mindset, and our passion for discovering new ways to teach math has led us to a life-changing friendship and collaboration. We are an unusual team. He's from Canada, and I'm from the United States. He eats volcanic-level spicy food, and I am on the much milder side. He listens to some pretty heavy music, while my ears lean toward the jazzier side of things (my recent evening with KISS aside), his sport preference is hockey (a dizzying whirlwind to me), mine baseball (a thinker's game ;)). However, the wonders of modern technology provided us an opportunity to chat in a Facebook group, exchange several similarly impassioned and oriented posts, and eventually discover that we were going to attend the same National Council of Teachers of Mathematics conference in April 2016 in San Francisco. We decided to meet before the conference and share a beer—a simple social act that will play a significant role in this book.

I mention this because it reminds me of the way I met and made friends in school. I moved to what is now my hometown, Fresno, California, in late summer of 1969, a kid not quite ready for fourth grade. I didn't know anyone, but in the first week or so, I had several encounters with guys, some of whom I remain in contact with and consider friends. Most of that friendship building, however, happened during recess. During that free play, we'd make up games, challenge each other's abilities, laugh, run, stumble about, skin knees and elbows, give and receive bruises, and generally just enjoy being alive. That same freedom, humor, and adventure has been characteristic of my friendship—and our first official collaboration—with Sunil. So many good things in my youth—and some of the best from my 50s—have grown out of the unstructured play of recess.

It might seem odd that we have chosen mathematics and specifically mathematics teaching as our focus for this book. This is a subject that is most often seen as being about structure, rigid adherence to rules, and a no-nonsense attitude toward reality that is mathematics in the hands of a former ski-bum and a court jester. In his wonderful book, *How Mathematicians Think: Using Ambiguity, Contradiction, and Paradox to Create Mathematics*, William Byers describes this phenomenon of seemingly antipodal juxtaposition as being what it takes to be creative in mathematics (and perhaps any field).

Sir Ken Robinson, a frequent speaker at conferences whose TED Talk video holds the record for most views, speaks at great length about how modern schooling is stifling creativity and society will be the worse for it. With this book, Sunil and I seek to proceed orthogonally from the present perception of mathematics and mathematics education. We plan to push in a direction that reveals mathematics as a creative, vibrant study with twists and turns like any good mystery novel. That is what we hope this book is for all who read it.

This is a book to take to the beach, to the pub, or to anywhere you hang with friends who enjoy an intellectual challenge. Interspersed throughout you will find conversations, some even real. Make no mistake, however: We are sounding a call, a siren's call if you will. We hope to lure you to our perspective, and yes, you should expect this call to ask you to embrace a disrupted future. A future in which mathematics education will no longer be characterized by mind-numbing hours of meaninglessly repetitive drudgery and proven ideas, but one in which mathematics is viewed rightly as a messy, noisy, playful human undertaking. We will also go further and lace that call with joy, mathematical for sure, but joy and hope for a brighter, if more openly constructed, future.

Subversive and Adventurous

I (Sunil) think we can reach that brighter future by remembering our past. Think back to your earliest school days and recall the sound of recess. That sound is universal. Doesn't matter where you are in the world. That sound of children's chatter, yelling, and screaming might seem harsh on the ears, but search "sounds of recess" on YouTube and you will get more than one hundred thousand results. Some of these videos are even titled "ambient background," clearly characterizing these sounds as happy and soothing. And why not? They are the sounds that inspire poetry. They are the sounds that inspire disruption.

It was during recess—a time with no agenda or order—that you and your friends could have all kinds of silly and daring conversations. Chris and I have certainly done that a time or two. Some of our most spirited conversations have been over beer while leisurely unpacking the magic of mathematics like laughing children.

What lies ahead of you in this book are fifty thousand words to rebuild, reconstruct, and reimagine the spirit of learning mathematics—and marry it, once and for all, to the natural curiosity and wonder of being a child. This marriage will not be a conventional union. Creative disruption doesn't settle for a traditional church wedding and lovely roast beef reception. It elopes to Las Vegas, gets married by an Elvis impersonator, and celebrates by playing $1 blackjack with locals on Fremont Street.

At its core, mathematics has always had a subversive and adventurous streak, but traditional educational institutions have shackled anything that lies outside the narrow domain of schoolhouse math. There simply hasn't been a whole lot of innovation since 'rithmetic came on the scene, and too many educational leaders have, unfortunately, deemed the subject closed, dead, and completely unearthed and exhausted. Don't take my word for it. Ask the millions of students who have learned to loathe mathematics thanks to boredom, confusion, and irrelevance during the past one hundred years.

Throw worksheets, homework, tests, and grades upon this miserable heap, and you get the tire fire that was twentieth-century math education. A chaotic snooze fest that riddled many kids—and their teachers—with anxiety. We speak in the past tense because, thanks to a new generation of math educators, we are steadily moving away from the narrow and linear narrative of drill and kill.

The progress is slow, not nearly the disruptive velocity needed to escape the anachronisms of the past. And having sympathetic parents hovering over their children doing math at home only adds to the negativity. According to a 2015 *New York Times* article, "Square Root of Kids' Math Anxiety: Their Parents' Help," a study published in *Psychological Science* found that first- and second-graders whose parents had math anxiety were learning less math and were more likely to develop their own math anxiety when their parents provided frequent help on their math homework. Researchers tested 438 students from twenty-nine public and private schools across three Midwestern states, finding a strong correlation between overly anxious parents and negative student performance. So much for good intentions.

The sad reality? Children are smothered. Children are coddled. Children are just bloody exhausted. And guess what? It is not just kids who suffocate and struggle in this environment; so does the subject they are presumably learning. Mathematics needs to breathe as well. The gulf between what students see and what they should see might as well be measured in light years.

Mathematics and children need time and space. Time for wondering and space for wandering. Mathematics education needs to start again with a new premise and a new promise: Mathematics is a joyful adventure of shared stories and experiences. Dancing on the embers of poorly photocopied worksheets and buzzkill tests will be the first order of business.

As referenced earlier, mathematics learning should not only sound like recess—everything from bubbly laughter to meditative silence—it should look like it too. Classrooms should and can look like math playgrounds. Shape blocks, Unifix® Cubes, puzzle books, math games, walls teeming with number lines and patterns created *by students*, some technological devices, riddles, conundrums, unsolved problems, open problems, symmetrical art, game theory, and so much more. All interwoven with the communal bliss of learning together.

The mathematical learning experience should recreate the awe and mouth-agape look on Charlie Bucket's face when he first saw the chocolate factory (just to be clear, we are talking about the spectacular 1971 Gene Wilder film, *Willy Wonka & the Chocolate Factory*, and not the creepy, futuristic reboot).

> *There is no life I know to compare to pure imagination. Living there you will be free if you truly wish to be.*
>
> —Willy Wonka

Happy Exploration

Traditional models of schools are prisons with very wide bars. Freedom is an illusion for both students and teachers. At some point, there is accountability to the unchecked authority of the past pedagogical practices. Standardized curriculum, outcomes, and expectations raise the bar for benign, factory efficiency—and lower it for everything else.

Our schools have, sadly, moved well beyond what Lockhart revealed to us in *A Mathematician's Lament*. The cheating that's happening not only enables a path to well-documented apathy, it deprives students of experiences that are empowering and emboldening—such as seeing the world through a lens of symmetry, beauty, and delight.

Mathematics is a bloody art form. At its heart, math is the messy fun of finger-painting. In 2017, Mitchel Resnick, director of the Lifelong Kindergarten group at the Massachusetts Institute of Technology Media Lab, released the timely book entitled *Lifelong Kindergarten*! In it Resnick espouses what he calls the "Four P's of Creative Learning," Projects, Peers, Passion, and Play. We see mathematics as a study in which all of these can be brought into everyone's experience. Although many passages from the book reverberate with the messages of this book, the following passage encapsulates the spirit of playfulness and the personal value of such exploration:

> *"Today, everyone needs to be a risk-taker, a doer, a maker of things—and not necessarily to bend the arc of history, but to bend the arc of their own lives."*

Children need to leave their thumbprints all over their journey of mathematics. Only then will there be a possibility of nurturing that most treasured goal—a lifetime interest in learning mathematics. Here too we both see a call for human flourishing, a call we are not alone in making either.

Math Recess aims to be the first math book that surfs the magnificent waves of joy that result from adopting a kindergarten mindset for K–12 math learning. Our plan is to deliver ideas, goals, hopes, and dreams of mathematics becoming one of the most loved subjects in school.

There is a long way to go. We are well past subtle and polite changes and far beyond merging ideas with the speed of erosion. We are just plain fed up with mathematics teaching that first appeases the desires and mandates of adults but is carefully disguised as a societal requirement for children. Do you think the fast introduction of worksheets, constant testing, and grades sounds like a construct for

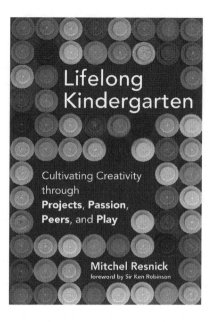

lifelong kindergarten? Quite the opposite. And, in the exact opposite direction we must run—for the sake of our children.

We are in the age of glorious disruption! Everything is up for debate. Everything is up for discussion. Everything needs to be rethought. Now. In mathematics education, that disruption will result in a classroom that is some wacky hybrid of entrepreneurial innovation centers and free-range Montessori-like exploration.

When I (Sunil) was in Austin, Texas, for a tech conference in 2018, I stayed at a hotel next to Capital Factory, a giant incubator and meetup for Texas entrepreneurs. There were glass walls everywhere. Every morning at breakfast, I would stare up at all those rooms filled with young, energetic people dreaming of changing the world.

Many K–12 educators hope for the same, but their creativity, communication, and connections are hindered by the limits of traditional school designs and philosophies.

There are, however, many signs of innovation. They occur on a daily basis when teachers like yourselves exhibit the patience and imagination necessary to guide the learning of mathematics with greater flexibility. These small actions, collectively, are helping create a larger movement away from the rigid ideas of the past.

Creating revolutionary ideas and championing *disruptive* children—who will imaginatively improve on these ideas—begins with reconstructing learning experiences that model how children want and need to learn in the future. It needs to be social, experiential, visual, auditory, and tactile. In other words, it needs to have an environment that is as joyful and playful as recess. It seems natural that having that kind of time and space in solving mathematics problems would aid in creating not only a deeper but also a much happier exploration. *Happier exploration is not a light goal.* It means discarding anxiety and nervousness when learning mathematics. This applies to both students and teachers—and not just elementary teachers but teachers at *all* levels.

The Struggle Is Real—and That's OK!

DrewR&R @drewfoster0 · 17m
Unacquainted adults ooze anxiety in maths sessions, hunched up shoulders dipped heads

Students do the exact same thing in many a maths lesson, until the magic moment the teacher has their trust... it's the "shoulders down" phase of the lesson... time to learn maths!

@Mathgarden

Drew Foster is an edtech specialist in England. He works with elementary- and middle-school students and teachers all the time. The shoulders-down posture is an important physical indication that a student is ready—truly ready—to learn mathematics. This is not a metaphor. It's a literal, observable phenomenon in math class. Think about it. A person's emotions are often visible to others, and teachers watch so many of them play out every day. Hunched shoulders indicate frustration, anxiety, even worry, and a relaxed shoulders-down posture—with arms swinging freely—indicates ease of mind and playfulness. Learning and exploring mathematics with marked anxiety is akin to digesting food under stress. It is an established fact that eating while anxious often hinders healthy digestion and presents a higher probability that food gets stored as toxins. Nothing beneficial happens during anxiety. This also applies to *digesting* mathematics.

Chris and I want all math classes to be filled with students assuming the shoulders-down posture. And you too! Whether you are an experienced middle-school teacher, a first-year elementary teacher, or an administrator, we want every essence and idea of this book to be approached with shoulders down. This will especially be asked of you when you get to some of the latter chapters in the book, as they will bring new and challenging ideas for many of you. There are no shortcuts in learning mathematics. For anyone. Everyone struggles with mathematics at various points in their lives. Struggle is the only way.

In December 2018, Thomas J. Williams, president of the North Carolina–based Strategic Educational Alliances, and former superintendent of education in North Carolina, tweeted one of my *Medium* articles. He referenced this idea of struggle and suggested it could be the mindset for everyone—teachers and parents—in forging new and emerging spaces for redefining math education.

Struggle does not have to feel isolated and riddled with anxiety. It can be, however, with the aid of this book, and a friend or two, lots of playful fun!

For this to occur, the math must be compelling, and time must be given. Some of the greatest mathematical mysteries took centuries

Thomas J. "Tom" Williams @tomwilliams777 · Dec 9

Like many Americans, I grew up thinking of myself as "not a math guy". This blog offers teachers/parents an attitude guide to change that. @ncssm @NCPrincipals "The Road To Learning Mathematics Goes Through Struggle, Not Efficiency" by @Mathgarden

FAILURE IS NOT THE OPPOSITE OF SUCCESS. IT IS **PART** OF SUCCESS.

The Road To Learning Mathematics Goes Through Struggle, Not Effi...
This past weekend, I found myself dragged down into the bleak hole of "Math Wars" debate on Twitter. None of the people who were bemoaning...
link.medium.com

and generations of mathematicians to solve. We, as math educators, have to collectively honor those efforts. Struggle never goes away in mathematics. It is its lifeblood.

I (Chris) recently met a mathematical artist from Portugal online. He does a fair amount of work using what is known as spherical conformal mapping or spherical perspective. He and I are in the same Facebook group, and he had posted photos of a few of his drawings. The comment that caught my eye was "Know the rules, break the rules!" That's the very essence of recess. It is in recess where we learn to make and break all kinds of rules.

To quote my co-author's *Medium* article, "If students are not actively engaged in mathematic struggle in safe and supportive environments, then they are not engaged in mathematical thinking. They are engaged in mathematical mimicking." The absence of struggle

Antonio Araujo shared a post.
December 3 at 11:20 PM

Sketching in spherical perspective, loosely based on the rules explained in my JMA paper. Loosely! Know the rules, break the rules! And the rules are: https://doi.org/10.1080/17513472.2018.1469378

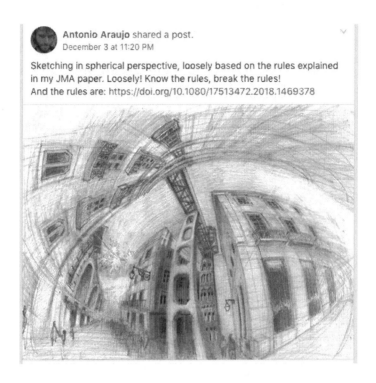

will create the absence of mathematical thinking. Efficiency was a twentieth-century idea linked to industrialization. Struggle is a twenty-first-century idea linked to humanization.

We must champion not only rule-breaking, but the struggles it might represent or bring about in the classroom. But struggle can only be championed in a safe environment. Safe simply means happy. Wouldn't it be nice if Bobby McFerrin's "Don't Worry Be Happy" could be part of a soundtrack to this kind of innovative learning? Of course, we would have to throw in the infectious samba rhythms of "Let the Children Play" by Santana!

My own memories of recess, from the 1970s, are kind of fuzzy, but I do remember that playing "foot hockey" with a tennis ball was a popular activity. When a tennis ball wasn't available—or it was kicked inadvertently under a portable—we used a chunk of ice.

(((Simon Fermor)))
@zapolator

Following

"The Road To Learning Mathematics Goes Through Struggle, Not Efficiency" - @Mathgarden
link.medium.com/kciMW3Z10R

QED

If students are not actively engaged in mathematical struggle in safe and supportive environments, then they are not engaged in mathematical thinking. They are engaged in mathematical mimicking.

The Road To Learning Mathematics Goes Th...
Sunil Singh

M

Improvisational thinking. The same kind of thinking that creates multiple strategies in solving a math problem. We also had names for our games involving hockey cards—topsies, farthies, and knocksies. If you had the coveted red utility ball at recess, you played four-square, a game that included moves like the "tea party" (going head-to-head with another student) and the "around-the-world" (ensuring clockwise or counter-clockwise movement of the ball). There were also yo-yos, skip ropes, hopscotch, tag, British Bulldog, swings, monkey bars, tetherball, school gossip, and just random running.

Recess was time spent on a playground, but it was also a portal to understanding and navigating the freedom and friendship we found within our emerging world. It was a time to test yourself, fall, get up, laugh or cry, and get up and go again. The metaphor of recess will be both explicit and implicit in our book. It is meant to reinforce our belief that mathematics is fun. Our use of recess throughout this book is a reminder that we must create classrooms and school environments that offer more time to play in the sandbox of numbers. Recall too that recess was a time where confusion got ironed out, where some misunderstandings seemed to explode then come back into focus; these also are part of the doing of mathematics, and keeping learners from them is to short-change the process.

Before any large-scale changes can occur, the mindset of teachers must change. Teachers must desire that change. Desire creates stamina and courage to go the extra mile to ensure what is the most important thing here—the mathematical well-being of our children.

We believe that students and teachers should want to run toward mathematics, not away from it, as has happened so often in the past. Every math teacher, regardless of experience, knowledge, and circumstances, can support the revolution that is already afoot. We hope this book reignites your love of mathematics and catalyzes change within you at the deepest level possible—your heart! Only that love has the power to reshape the purpose for learning mathematics in this age of creative disruption.

We recognize that this book will be used within the contexts of your lives, your work, and most likely, your schools. As is often the case with books for teachers, we will include a few discussion questions at the end. We have intentionally not pigeonholed activities by grade. Every class is different. The latitude for exploring many of these topics rests mainly on basic arithmetic. Feel free to break the rules of the game and ignore them, but you should know that we felt free to break the rules and include a smattering of unexpected and thought-provoking questions.

The bell is ringing. It's time for math recess!

QUESTIONS FOR DEEPER DISCUSSION

1. How can you make room in your perception of mathematics for playfulness and fun?

2. During the next week describe to a friend your first thoughts what a playful, loud, fun math lesson might entail.

3. In the context of your school or schooling more broadly, what rules do you perceive that need breaking?

Added Introduction
FOR TEACHERS AND SCHOOL ADMINISTRATORS IN THE USA

We are writing this book with the intention of altering mindsets toward what mathematics is taught, and how it is approached. Some of what we discuss will also touch on your own relationship with mathematics. We are writing this book as a resource for you in your own teaching. Throughout the text, we will point out intersections between our topics and the 2010 version of the Common Core State Standards in Mathematics (CCSSM). Because this book is not targeted to any specific grade level, it would be impossible to consistently align the topics we showcase to Content Standards. Therefore, we will focus on the Standards of Mathematical Practice (SMPs) as the overarching themes for our play. I (Chris) have been working in the field of professional development of teachers at all grade levels, both inservice and preservice, for the past eighteen years. I have had extensive experience with the CCSSM as they were developed, enthusiastically adopted, called into question, and are now being somewhat accepted in this current period of detente.

The SMPs represent the broad goals, the deep reasons behind why we as a society value mathematical education; they also are the same across every grade level and are meant to be addressed through every set of Content Standards. The Content Standards are among the most debated and, as Sunil is fond of saying, "They go up and down, like a toilet seat." Consider the inclusion of long division of polynomials. Even our good friend and Exploding Dots provocateur James Tanton struggled to understand the inclusion of this standard. Many content standards exist for reasons obscured from those who teach them, often coming off as being included because "that's what we have always done."

Sunil and I see mathematics not as collection of individual skills—knowing the quadratic equation—or bits of information—which numbers are irrational. We believe it's a collection of mental practices, attitudes, and, yes, tools that we as a species have developed in our quest to understand the world. It is a veritable mental playground where you practice, play, argue, fight, and struggle, then ultimately resolve and understand. These are the goals of becoming mathematical.

Few arguments are levied at the substance of the SMPs; however, it is for example nigh on impossible to formulate a cogent argument against the goal that all students should be able to "make sense of problems and persevere in solving them." That is not to say that these standards are flawless, or even particularly well written, but the goals pointed to, the dream of education these standards produce, do provide teachers a "North Star" to guide their efforts.

Here they are in case you haven't read them recently. These are the "varieties of expertise mathematics educators at all levels should seek to develop in their students" (corestandards.org/Math/Practice). Each begins with the phrase, "Mathematically proficient students …"

1. **Make sense of problems and persevere in solving them:** This is an essential practice when doing mathematics because math is not about repetition of the same process over and over again. It is about applying knowledge to new problems. Sense-making is at the core of humanity's quest,

and we have been pursuing it throughout our evolutionary history. That is perseverance.

2. **Reason abstractly and quantitatively:** There is no small amount of controversy over these ideas being put together as a single practice. Reasoning abstractly encompasses a range of behaviors from making drawings of situations to expressing relationships using algebra but also much more. Reasoning quantitatively is different. Here students could be asked to think in pure magnitudes or proportions.

3. **Construct viable arguments and critique the reasoning of others:** Answers to "How do you know?" and "Can you defend that?" are the simplest examples of this practice. It also includes the idea of mathematical proof.

4. **Model with mathematics:** Mathematical modeling is among the most important applications of mathematics. In its most advanced applications it means building mathematical expressions that can be used to predict behavior of complex systems such as the stock market or the long-term performance of a baseball team. In its most basic form, this practice can entail a child collecting data and modeling it mathematically to predict how tall a stack of cups will be or how many copies of a repeated pattern of blocks it takes to cover an area on their desk.

5. **Use appropriate tools strategically:** This can be confusing. What are the tools of mathematics? What are the appropriate versus inappropriate uses? Tools of mathematics are both mental and physical. Mental tools include reasoning, pattern seeking and describing, expressing in models, algebra, logic, and so forth. Physical tools include calculators, computers, paper and pencil, the internet, and

so forth. Knowing when and when not to use any of these is part of the learning process of becoming mathematically literate in the twenty-first century.

6. **Attend to precision:** Precision in mathematics has at least two meanings important in the educational setting. First, it is a concept inherently important in understanding and conducting measurement. Precision matters when reporting measurements, and it takes developed judgment to determine various levels of precision. Would the best units of measurement for distance be centimeters, meters, or parsecs? Second, precision is also related to the language we use. Here a student might need to decide whether it is enough to know that the image they are looking at is a quadrilateral or whether it will make a difference to know that it is also an isosceles trapezoid.

7. **Look for and make use of structure:** We will be showing many examples of this throughout this book. An aspect we will focus on will be the structure of numbers. What are the general attributes of all numbers regardless of how they are represented (base ten, base two, as magnitudes etc.)? What are the attributes of numbers that vary? You often hear people say that they can tell an even number just by looking at the last (right most) digit and checking whether it is one of five digits (0, 2, 4, 6, or 8); however, this is dependent on expressing those numbers in base ten. In base two, an even number is any number that ends in 0. Period; that's it. So this is a structural element that is contextually defined.

8. **Look for and express regularity in repeated reasoning:** In 1994 Keith Devlin, who many are familiar with as the Math Guy on NPR (though he is by no means limited

to this role), wrote a book entitled *Mathematics: The Science of Patterns*. Pattern is inherently a part of what mathematicians exploit as they investigate, describe, and attempt to codify what they see in the universe we all inhabit. It is such a powerful tool when used wisely. This is part of the practice of expressing regularity in repeated reasoning. There are other aspects as well. Later in this book I will describe a proof that argues there are an infinite number of prime numbers. To do so, I will employ a pattern of reasoning that is one of the oldest in the mathematician's arsenal, *reductio ad absurdum*. Mathematics and mathematical thinking can push those who engage in it deep into "meta" thinking, and this is also a skill or practice every student should be exposed to and can learn from.

One further caveat, and this is a personal one for me. Perseverance in solving problems does not mean that a student makes it to the end of a one-hundred-item worksheet without giving up and crying. Perseverance does mean a willingness to sit with discomfort and wrestle with an idea until your mind brings it into submission. You will not see any examples of worksheets (or "shut up sheets" as they have been dubbed) ready for you to take back to your classroom.

With these practices in mind, we encourage you to let yourself play. Along the way, we will endeavor to point out some of the connections we see on the mathematical playground we set before you. You are encouraged to find others because we will surely miss some, probably most. We have faith in you, the readers, to plumb the depths, skin your knees, climb the heights, and on occasion, break the rules.

From time to time, in [square brackets] you will see a reference such as [SMP: 1, 3, 5] next to a problem investigation or figure. This indicates that those ideas contained are related to a specific Standard of Mathematical Practice. Dog ear this page now so you can flip back and forth to know what we mean.

BRIEF STATEMENTS OF THE SMPS:

Mathematically proficient students will...

1. Make sense of problems and persevere in solving them

2. Reason abstractly and quantitatively

3. Construct viable arguments and critique the reasoning of others

4. Model with mathematics

5. Use appropriate tools strategically

6. Attend to precision

7. Look for and make sense of structure

8. Look for and express regularity in repeated reasoning

CHAPTER 1
Just Play

Mathematics is not a language.
It is an adventure.

—Paul Lockhart

As a kid growing up in the 1970s (Sunil), my house backed up to a park. That park bled right into the public school that I attended. There were days I would walk out the front of the house and take the sidewalk path to school. Other days, I purposely skipped out the backyard into the wide expanse of the park. If I remember correctly, those were either snowy and icy winter days or rainy and muddy spring days. A small gully that led all the way to one of the school's portables—which would be home to my grade four class and those awful-smelling bean plants—was my school walk distraction. In cold weather, I would find patches of ice to slide along (or accidentally put my boot through for a *soaker*). In the warmth of April rain, I threw popsicle sticks into this pop-up river to see which one could travel the furthest without getting stuck.

This before-school ritual, which lasted several *seasons*, is one of my most lasting and cherished memories of childhood—improvisational play that was unwatched and unadulterated. The entire history of mathematics has a similar narrative. What do you think came before lightbulb epiphanies, notoriety, and success? Lots of mucking around, trial and error, a few Hail Marys, and gobs of time and space! The world of imagination that lives—well, *can* live—in our heads is where mathematics dwells as well.

The idea of play in mathematics has become prevalent in many curriculum documents throughout North America, giving proof that the value of one of the most innate and instinctive attributes of childhood is anchoring the future of math education. The Next Generation Learning Standards for the State of New York (full implementation by 2020) sees play as a foundational piece in the key K–3 years.

> Play is listed multiple times in the Standards. This is an intentional effort to remain within developmentally appropriate parameters that do not pit play against "academic" learning.

> **It is also a reminder that passive approaches such as seat work, worksheets, scripted programs, and rote learning are antithetical to play-based paradigm for learning.**

> Instruction that is integrated, multisensory, and play-based, captures children's imagination. Skills or content are not taught in isolation, but as essential components of lessons about the child's word with attention paid to what may be relevant to his or her interests. Structured to offer children ample opportunity for self-expression through varied media, instruction in the early childhood classroom regularly employs art, music, performance, and imaginative play.

Mathematics, just as creative a discipline as the arts, develops many of the required skills of "thinking mathematically" through play. Without the introduction to mathematical play early on, students will navigate a narrow and unstable terrain for the mathematics that will follow—and their natural creativity will predictably atrophy.

Imagination + Mathematics = Play

In 2017, Chris and I went to the annual National Council of Supervisors of Mathematics Conference in San Antonio. We both attended a presentation by James Tanton, one of the founders of The Global Math Project. Later in the book, we will uncrate some of his magnificent Exploding Dots. The presentation was a delightful hodgepodge of mathematical play and explored how this kind of play often *avoids hard work*. That's right. If you know how to play with the math in front of you, you can make your life a helluva lot easier! Play is fun, but it also is straight-up practical.

It is a happy talent to know how to play.

—Ralph Waldo Emerson

One of the first questions that Tanton shared with his Texas audience was this rather innocent looking subtraction question:

```
 1 0 0 1
-  7 8 3
```

Almost all of us have been taught—conditioned—to begin the standard subtraction algorithm. For a student learning this long subtraction method, the zeros might trigger that quiet gulp of needing to *borrow* across these "empty numbers" until there is a digit that can be pilfered for some needed coinage. You might notice my explanation quickly drifted into slang, but children need initial explanations that fit their vocabulary and understanding. There is no borrowing going on here. None. You never give back—you only take! The practice is, technically, a redistribution, but that word does not inspire the imaginations of young students. Before we get into a most playful hack of this generally uninteresting problem, let's explain the standard algorithm with a relatable story.

Most kids will understand that because this is subtraction, there is some idea of depletion going on here. The 1 needs to be reduced by 3—now might be a good time to plant a seed in the kids' heads about negative numbers. So the 1 is a *little light*. It goes over to its neighbor in the tens. Nope. Got nothing for you. It then hops on over to the hundreds. Same sad story. Finally, over in the mighty thousands column, there is some relief for our subtraction dilemma. We snatch it! At the same time, we are going to pull a Robin Hood and redistribute our bounty. *Redistribute* being the optimal verb here.

As we make our way back, we have some starving 0s to contend with. When we are at the hundreds, we should be looking at our one thousand as ten hundreds. Guess what? Because we only want to take what we will eventually need, we give nine of our hundreds to this 0. We then move on over to the tens with our last remaining hundred. Once again we are at the tens, so we make a necessary conversion so that we can say we have ten tens. Same situation. We gladly give this zero all our tens but one, and we finally we arrive back home with one ten—all that we needed. Now we have a total of eleven (10 + 1), and this is more than enough to take away the patiently waiting 3.

Yes. That was a long story. We could—heck, we *already do*—just give kids mysterious steps of slashing out numbers with that mangled use of the word *borrowing*. Those numbers lose all meaning when kids do questions like these. Intuition takes a hike, and mild fear swoops in as students confusingly navigate the deficiencies of the minuend. I certainly did. I'd see a string of zeros and frantically remind myself, "Make the 0 a 9. Make the 0 a 9. Make the 0 a 9...." like some cultish chant.

A smarter idea would be to start adding up from 783 to 1001. I have always taught my kids whenever possible, to add up from one "goal post" to the other. In this case it would look like 17 + 200 + 1. The picture is one of several dozen I have done with my kids to reinforce the idea of flexibility in obtaining richer math fact fluency.

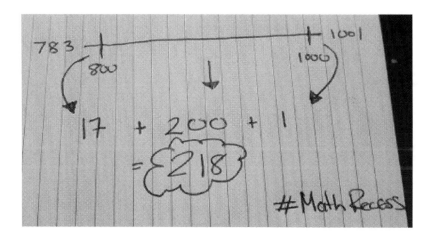

An equally smart idea, as demonstrated by Tanton in his workshop, was to reconstruct the question to make it simpler—subtract 2 from both numbers. Now the question is 999 subtract 781. No stressful encounter with the long subtraction algorithm while simultaneously banking another technique of making your life mathematically easier! [SMP 7 was used here; employing an understanding of the structure of the number system is always a goal over rote memorization of algorithm.]

The myriad of unexplained steps throughout K–12 mathematics creates an understanding that has less stability than a Jenga game. It also leaves a negative residue surrounding what it means to do mathematics—almost as if mathematics is something *done unto them*—and only moves our community of learners further and further away from the adventure that is mathematics. An adventure that every student is entitled to experience.

What should be a leisurely walk in the sun is more like a miserable march in the cold rain. That's why I keep pounding Lockhart's adventure theme constantly on Twitter.

 **Sunil Singh**
@Mathgarden

If we as educators do not believe this and show this, then the discrete experiences students have with mathematics will not sum up to the journey they should have been promised. @fjmubeen @MathWithMatthew @MathforLove @noasbobs @Stephen_Hurley @stepanpruch @Dean_of_math

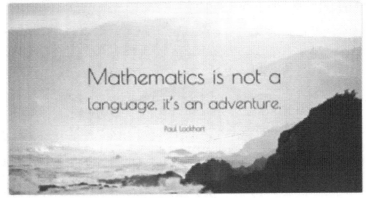

Mathematics is not a language, it's an adventure.

Paul Lockhart

Reason #99 to Play

All of this could be easily avoided if we gave students the deeper understanding of mathematics that they deserve. Why not simply, for the love of God, just let them play?

Having lived in Canada now for close to fifty years, I (Sunil) can confirm that yes, hockey runs deep in the cultural psyche from coast to coast. To the surprise of nobody, Wayne Gretzky—whose retired number of 99 is an iconic reminder to the world of his athletic talents—has been hailed by most in the sporting world as the greatest hockey player of all time. Hence his nickname, the *Great One*.

Gretzky wasn't the biggest. He wasn't the fastest. He was simply the most damn creative player the game has ever seen—and will probably ever see. Gretzky was driven by passion and love for the game. How did he get there? He certainly had some natural-born instinct, but there was also lots and lots and lots of *play*.

Gretzky has commented on the current state of the game and how it is overcoached with too much emphasis on positional play and drills. All of those are important, but only if they do not jeopardize the fun and joy of the game. Gretzky honed his skills on those mythical Canadian ponds and backyard rinks. He said it was as simple as throwing some pucks on the ice and letting kids create their own games.

The current state of mathematics is akin to the hockey culture that Gretzky bemoans. Too little play and zero fun. Our current system of math education is not set up to invoke creative play and hopefully produce many *Wayne Gretzkys* of mathematics. It just doesn't have mental and physical freedom to try out new content, weird strategies, and divergent ideas. More like industrious players who are conditioned to play with simple and choreographed strategies. I doubt they will have the mindset—and risk—to try new ideas and tactics.

They will likely lack the imagination to bank the puck off the boards at surprising angles to create new passing lanes—*sort of like adjusting a subtraction question to avoid hard work.*

That kind of deep understanding of hockey comes from playing and practicing in a fun environment over and over again. Practice had to be fun for Gretzky. It was the only way he would practice. An unhealthy and unwarranted separation of practice and fun has led to unnecessary discussions about when and how much to practice mathematics. If it is fun, students will want to practice, and contrary to popular belief, fun doesn't have to be easy. Math facts, the absolute critical foundation for building math knowledge, must be built joyously! When Chris and I were in San Jose, California, for the Global Math Project Kickoff Symposium in October 2018, Jo Boaler

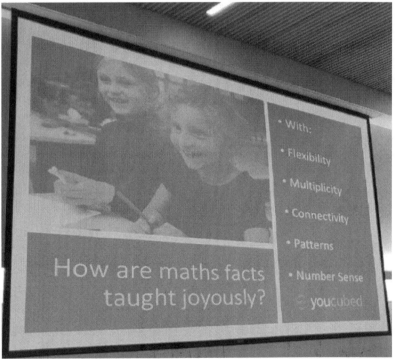

Jo Boaler's Presentation at Global Math Project Symposium, San Jose, California.

reminded us precisely of this idea in her afternoon presentation. Many of her slides involving numbers were beautiful, colorful relationships between them—inviting us all to see that the fluency of math facts is paved with colorful connections.

This is how someone like Wayne Gretzky would appreciate learning mathematics—employing multiple ideas and having fun. Maybe if we continue to embrace teaching math with such a spirit, more and more kids will carry on learning the subject with infectious alacrity!

The Exploding Dots experience that so much of the world first saw in October 2017 as part of Global Math Week was aligned to the belief of how Gretzky envisioned the game of hockey—a game to be played and enjoyed. In fact, it is emphasized throughout the various islands of the website (expodingdots.org). It is also the only button that is emphasized with an exclamation mark. Millions of people from all over the world are constantly being alerted that this is the *real end game of mathematics.*

Further Explanation M

The Traditional Division Algorithm N

Division by 10 O

Wild Exploration P

Just play!

You make it boring and you will lose so many creative/talented thinkers. Kids don't hate mathematics because it's hard; they hate it because it is so bloody boring. Math facts and drills will have their currency raised if there is a creative game to play and feel impassioned about. If facts and drills are just the *end game*, don't be too shocked when kids drift away from wanting to learn about mathematics. Even the standard times tables chart is ripe with obvious and not-so-obvious patterns. Look at the 9 × 9 table below. Why is there only one digit in each square?

○	1	2	3	4	5	6	7	8	9
1	1	2	3	4	5	6	7	8	9
2	2	4	6	8	1	3	5	7	9
3	3	6	9	3	6	9	3	6	9
4	4	8	3	7	2	6	1	5	9
5	5	1	6	2	7	3	8	4	9
6	6	3	9	6	3	9	6	3	9
7	7	5	3	1	8	6	4	2	9
8	8	7	6	5	4	3	2	1	9
9	9	9	9	9	9	9	9	9	9

We will explore this in more detail in later in the book, but each entry is the digital root of the number that would have been there. For example, 7 × 5 = 35 and 3 + 5 = 8. These digital roots are important for checking sums and using the pattern of nines to simply find digital roots of large numbers (casting out nines). We need to keep students excited and glued to the rich patterning that is everywhere in mathematics. Competency alone is not a rubric for retaining interest. [SMP: 2; just look at all the abstraction being accomplished here, and SMP: 7.] (We won't always make extensive notes in the future but will at times just state the SMP being addressed.)

Organized sports, which attracts millions of kids across North America for its intrinsic fun and social outlet, is not immune from shocking attrition rates once the fun is subtracted and the pressure to win is added.

In 2016, *The Washington Post* reported that 70 percent of children were leaving organized sports, a mass exodus from something that was once pure play and was now pure drill and expectation. I am sure mathematics has, at the very least, those harsh percentages of disapproval. The only difference is that kids are free to leave the anxious, frustrating, and pressure-filled environments of the soccer field, baseball diamond, and hockey rink.

In math classes, they are held captive for a few more years. It's like being trapped in an excruciatingly long timeshare presentation of condos in Del Boca Vista—that are being sold with the urgency as though they were oxygen. When did something like subtracting fractions with denominators beyond 5 *become interesting and critical*? When we start the hard sale on mathematics with overstretched and overbaked ideas like this, the attrition rates for learning mathematics become magnified. Some students simply stop trusting those educators who are making the sales pitch. The communication channels of teaching lose their potency. Trust, as we will see later in the book, is the fabric and foundation for empowering change in math education.

The intentions might be noble—I said *might*—but the overall arid presentation in anachronistic seating arrangements that is labored with unrelenting macro and micro testing is *more oxygen sucking than oxygen providing*. Mathematics is a wild, living, and breathing entity. We have caged it—along with our students—and there will be consequences. If you think this metaphor is harsh, talk to young teenagers who used to love the sports they played. The most important goal of participating in organized sports—to create a lifetime of physical activity for pleasure—is ironically compromised. Play and fun is the lifeblood of athletics. Play and fun is also the lifeblood for *mathletics*. There can be no compromises.

Be Good with Math

A preposition changes everything. Schools, teachers, and parents have always wanted their students to be good "at" math. That goal, while earnest, has not only ruined how students explore mathematics, it has ruined any deep questions around the scope and purpose of mathematics. Getting our students to be good in the narrow domain of K–12 mathematics—even the championed practicality is toothless in a world that operates as a complicated game of commerce, risk assessment, and *house* edge—automatically creates and supports a culture of every educator taking this same narrow path. Getting *good* becomes etched in the consciousness of math education. It becomes almost impossible to remove.

So much volume is taken up by this, hardly any room remains for anything else. Little time for math history. Little time for learning *new* content—that desire is collectively quashed by trying to master a tired canon of twentieth-century thinking in math education. Little time to focus on equity issues. Little time for the most important idea involved in teaching any subject—knowing and *wanting to know* your students.

All the energy of math education becomes invested in a proven model of, quite ironically, failure. This anxious and exhaustive focus on getting good has always led to unchecked failure. But don't ask me. Ask the countless kids who have had such negative experiences of being weighed down by routines, practice, and testing. Come to think of it, are we even asking them? If we are not, why not?

The bottom line? If we are not changing the content and approach to learning mathematics to the rich playfulness that students and teachers deserve, then we need to at least stop making it compulsory. I even got Dan Meyer to retweet this idea and throw some flames in for good measure—alerting the Twitter folks that the reading road ahead will be straight-up provocative and *least traveled*. Meyer has been a leader in contemporary math education for over a decade now. His seminal 2010 TED Talk, "Math Class Needs a Makeover," helped inspire a math revolution that continues today.

Dan Meyer
@ddmeyer

Following ⌄

"If we cannot convince students of the shattering magnificence of math after 8 years, students have the right to terminate their learning." 🔥🔥🔥 from @Mathgarden

Six Questions That Math Educators Need To Answer Honestly
I taught long enough to realize that education's primary mandates are financial and political — they have been unspoken cornerstones for…

If there were one person that we all could channel in our math classrooms, I would have to choose Fred Rogers. This was confirmed after watching the brilliant documentary (99 percent on Rotten Tomatoes) *Won't You Be My Neighbor?* on a plane to a math conference in California in the fall of 2018. Rogers might have been gentle, kind, and warm, but he was disruptor when it came to television. He constantly broke new ground by sticking to leisurely, happy play. The most authentic learning of any kind happens in such an environment, mathematics notwithstanding.

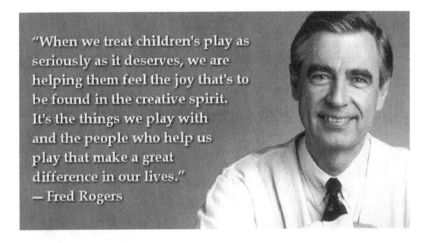

"When we treat children's play as seriously as it deserves, we are helping them feel the joy that's to be found in the creative spirit. It's the things we play with and the people who help us play that make a great difference in our lives."
— Fred Rogers

It is important that teachers see the value of play in mathematics. In early grades, this often means playing games. The history of games in society has crossed every culture in the past one thousand years. Two of the most central ideas of the benefits of playing games have been social connection and teaching. That is why playing games in math class has both explicit and implicit value. Many of the math games presented in this book employ a strategy to win, which can only be attained after observing several outcomes, pattern and repeated play. When students can articulate and appreciate these strategies, they are developing the general strategy skills that are employed in every math problem that they will encounter.

Sprouts

So many wonderful activities can fully illustrate the long trajectory and value of mathematical play, especially with the advent of some great technological applications. In keeping with the first rule of old-school recess—you don't need a lot of stuff to have fun—we wanted the first activity to anchor the symbolic ideas of this book to be one that was created during a simpler but pivotal time: the 1960s-era game Sprouts. That it was co-created by one of the giants of mathematical thinking, John Conway, significantly factors into its selection as the entry into serious mathematical fun.

Sprouts is a simple game to play. All you need is paper and a pencil. Back in 1967, this game, which had some rather heavy mathematical ideas deeply embedded in its structure, was popularized by the late Martin Gardner in his "Mathematical Games" column in *The Scientific American*. Here is a quote by Conway addressing the popularity of the game half-a-century ago.

> The day after sprouts sprouted, it seemed that everyone was playing it; at coffee or tea times, there were little groups of people peering over ridiculous to fantastic sprout positions.

More than a decade ago, Paul Lockhart championed Sprouts as a game for students to actively explore to further their burgeoning mathematical curiosities. He framed his argument in a hypothetical interview in which he took a Devil's Advocate position (Simplicio) of challenging his own beliefs:

SIMPLICIO: Then what should we do with young children in math class?

SALVIATI: Play games! Teach them Chess and Go, Hex and Backgammon, Sprouts and Nim, whatever. Make up a game. Do puzzles. Expose them to situations where deductive reasoning is necessary. Don't worry about notation and technique, help them to become active and creative mathematical thinkers. [SMP: 1, 8, with a touch of 3]

Activity 1: Sprouts

Sprouts is played by two players connecting spots with lines on a playing surface. The playing surface (piece of paper or computer screen) begins with n spots for the players to choose between. Three spots are usually a good starting point. Players take turns connecting spots (or drawing from a spot to itself) and adding a new spot along the drawn lines with the following constraints:

- The line must not touch or cross itself or any other line
- The new spot cannot be on an endpoint of the line, and thus splits the line into two parts
- No spot can have more than three lines connected to it; note that when a new spot is created, it starts with two lines already connected to it. Eventually, there are no legal moves. The last player to make a legal move wins.

Reference Link: nrich.maths.org/2413

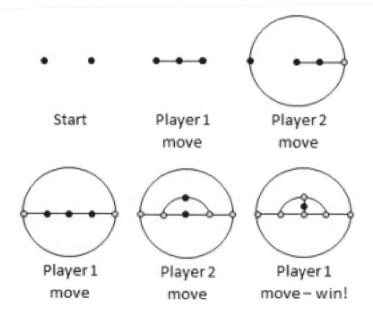

If you would like to see a nice video illustrating actual gameplay, find the links below:

Recreational Math—Game of Sprouts
bit.do/mathrecess

The dots don't have to line up, and the lines don't have to be straight or perfectly curved. It's just easier to see the gameplay in this tidier demonstration. The beautiful thing about Sprouts is that no game can ever end in a draw. That means there is an optimal strategy for going first or second when there are a specific number of dots to start the game. We will let you and your students discover them! Folded into this optimal strategy is some tidy algebra and even the concept that this game is NP-Complete, a term that, in the simplest sense, means that the time it would take a computer to figure out the solution is a very long time.

This is one of many fun math games children can explore early on that has rich complexities nested into its structure—complexities they will perhaps discover later in their mathematical lives. As we will find out, the exploratory play that is fundamental in a game like Sprouts eventually leads to discovering new and magical kingdoms in mathematics. Truncating any part of this galvanizing adventure will reduce the chances that students and teachers see the larger landscape of mathematics. The journeys are their own, but students will only remain in control if they are given ample space to play.

The Currency of Freedom

You don't have to go far to find universally respected authority on the benefits of recess and its associated freedom. The following is an opening excerpt from a July 2007 article, "The Importance of Play in Promoting Healthy Child Development and Maintaining Strong Parent-Child Bonds," that appeared in the *American Academy of Pediatrics*:

> Play allows children to use their creativity while developing their imagination, dexterity, and physical, cognitive, and emotional strength. Play is important to healthy brain development. It is through play that children at a very early age engage and interact in the world around them. Play allows children to create and explore a world they can master, conquering their fears while

practicing adult roles, sometimes in conjunction with other children or adult caregivers. As they master their world, play helps children develop new competencies that lead to enhanced confidence and the resiliency they will need to face future challenges. Undirected play allows children to learn how to work in groups, to share, to negotiate, to resolve conflicts, and to learn self-advocacy skills. When play is allowed to be child driven, children practice decision-making skills, move at their own pace, discover their own areas of interest, and ultimately engage fully in the passions they wish to pursue. Ideally, much of play involves adults, but when play is controlled by adults, children acquiesce to adult rules and concerns and lose some of the benefits play offers them, particularly in developing creativity, leadership, and group skills. In contrast to passive entertainment, play builds active, healthy bodies. Perhaps above all, play is a simple joy that is a cherished part of childhood.

Let's just zero in on that last sentence. If nothing else, happy memories are the products of unbounded discovery and exploration.

Building Better Memories of Math

It's been fifteen years since Paul Lockhart fired his shot-heard-around-the-world at math education in the form of his then underground essay, *A Mathematician's Lament* (which formally became a book 5 years later). For most educators, that shot was either a direct hit or a complete miss. I (Sunil) fell into the former category—so much so, that my first book, *Pi of Life*, references Lockhart five times from his first book. Below is one of his most jarring reminders of what traditional math education has done to too many students...

> I don't see how it's doing society any good to have its members walking around with vague memories of algebraic formulas and geometric diagrams, and clear memories of hating them.

One of the things Lockhart strongly refers to throughout in *A Mathematician's Lament* is the negative impact that current methods of math education continue to have on students. And then, there is the above quote, in which he touches on a word that is often undervalued in evaluating the currency of mathematics—*memories.* I feel lucky that I don't have any negative memories. At the same time, in close to five hundred hours of math education, I don't have too many that are positive. I did well in math throughout school, but my experience of school mathematics was benign. I simply don't have any positive memories of mathematics that involved creativity, memorable discussions, surprises, or cool diversions. I have memories of doing well at whatever it was I was supposed to be doing well at—answering a bucket load of *what* questions.

More than a decade later, with the engine of social media fueling deeper reflection about why and how we teach mathematics—all this now marinating in familiar approaches to education found in countries like Finland—there is an almost moral imperative to teach mathematics with an endgame that completely rewrites what mathematical memories students should now have.

I (Chris) was one of the first kids on my block whose parents owned a handheld calculator. Yeah. I am that old. My father was a soil chemist, and as such, he needed, on occasion, to crunch numbers and had purchased the device for work. I give him credit to this day for not being afraid to let his twelve-year-old son "play" with it. I was fascinated by its glowing red LEDs and chunky, clunky buttons. He kept a handy supply of nine-volt batteries, because this thing gobbled them up like they were ice cream at a birthday party.

At any rate, this device was not terribly fancy by today's standards. It had all four operations, stored a single number in memory, and had a square and a square root function. At the time that I started playing with it, I had very little idea what square root really meant. I came to discover this, however, by piddling around with the calculator while the San Francisco Giants baseball game was advertising Schlitz beer. I'd spend a large amount of time trying out numbers, adding and subtracting, and squaring and unsquaring, especially. Then I discovered the power of the ability to store a number in memory. That calculator and the freedom my dad gave me to play with it convinced me that I could understand numbers. Years later when I was failing my Algebra 1 and Algebra 2 classes in school, I never lost confidence that I could understand math. The problem was that my teachers didn't see or value the same math that I did.

I was not a successful student in school. My wife likes to tell the story of how I had to make a deal with my high school counselor just so I could graduate. I never fully bought into the way schools were designed or implemented. I loved to learn but hated to sit on my butt all day just regurgitating drivel that seemed both trivial and a tad obvious if you just put your mind to it. I did little homework, made poor grades, and during my senior year could often be found on my back on a bench outside of a classroom, watching clouds fly by or eating a cinnamon roll.

I've always thought it interesting that the only math class I enjoyed in high school was geometry, because we were allowed to play with shapes, discover relationships, and describe them with this beautiful notation. One of my teachers, Mr. Tom "Jake" Jacobson, would encourage me to play with facts, conjecture, and "puzzle it out."

Having grown up knowing that I could play with the thoughts and concepts in math gave me the confidence to tackle it, even in the face of past failing grades.

Making Math Matter

In January 2017, Francis Su raised the bar for learning mathematics with his moving and emotional talk as outgoing president of the Mathematical Association of America. His talk was about living a flourishing life filled with virtue, and it focused on his friend named Christopher. Christopher is serving prison time for armed robbery. The heart of Su's talk centered around the comment, "When we think of mathematics, do we think of Christopher?" Immediately the radius of equity, empathy, and humanity in learning mathematics was increased dramatically for all in the audience. And for us as well. In 2018, five years after he started communicating with Christopher, Francis finally met his friend in person. A book, *Mathematics is for Human Flourishing*, has been written by Su, documenting that relationship and the loftiest ideas for learning mathematics.

If we do not at least temper our collective objectives with those of Su's timely call, this would not only be a critical error in re-calibrating mathematics' human purpose, but it would ensure that Paul Lockhart's quote regarding mathematical memories continues to be sadly victorious.

Although I (Sunil) don't have too many rich memories of mathematics—specifically math teachers—I do have vivid memories of one of my high-school teachers. That would be Mr. Scott, who taught history. I can *still* recite whole passages of Napoleon's battle strategies, the bloody mayhem of the Assyrians, and horrific conditions of soldiers in World War I. The reasons I can do this are complex but can be distilled down to some key elements. First, the best way to teach is through storytelling, and mathematics is not occluded from being presented in such a fashion. Au contraire. *Mathematics is history.* Period. Weaving in its thematic development gives math its human colors and repudiates the notion that it was popped out of a can or created in test tubes or some other sterile manufacturing. We will delve deeper into this reality in a later chapter.

Students need to feel engaged by true and honest mathematical conversations. They also need teachers who will show them empathy and provide them with time and space to build mathematical curiosity and literacy in their learning. Students need to feel emboldened by mathematics. Mr. Scott was the most engaging teacher I ever had—we clung to his every word, even to the most frivolous details. He had empathy for us. He understood us as teenagers, and he taught history that resonated with our sensibilities without compromising the historical truths and facts. Our lives were greater for having experienced such a passionate teacher.

Thirty-five years later, I am referencing this experience to bolster our argument for the need to reshape mathematical education and gently push it into more expansive and immersive environments. We believe this pushing can bring mathematics back to what it was always envisioned to be. Think about the qualities that a mathematician values:

Persistence
Communication
Resilience
Critical thinking
Logic
Curiosity
Creativity
Organization
Collaboration

Now consider how the concept of *play* relates to the healthy development of each one of these critical markers for deep mathematical thinking. My entire "career" of recess and associated play contributed to each of these bullet points. Using a chunk of ice instead of a tennis ball—creativity. Playing four-square with one ball and twelve kids—organization. Playing British Bulldog in the snow with constant tackling—resilience. Now imagine pairing the valuable characteristics of a mathematician with the fertile playground of recess. Willy Wonka's head would be bursting with imagination!

Mastery. Competency. Understanding. These should be minimum standards for mathematics going forward, for they alone will not create lasting impressions of a rich mathematical experience. That would simply mirror what I experienced—good intentions that were boring.

That might have been okay a few generations ago. It's not anymore. Mathematics is getting more and more recognized as a shared, human experience—whose greatest moments occur between the question and the answer. Let's give our students a happy and joyful experience with mathematics, so that many years from now, when they reflect on their memories of mathematics, they have ones that are positive—proving that we did succeed in communicating the human essence of mathematics.

QUESTIONS FOR DEEPER DISCUSSION

1. What is an optimal strategy for winning Sprouts with three dots? With four?

2. Recall a subject within your educational process that made you feel like you were playing. What was it about that subject and the specific activities being used that made it so playful and so much fun? How could you replicate that in other areas of learning?

3. How could you create a space at your school where mathematical games and play are options for children, not merely as rewards but as part of regular practice?

CHAPTER 2

Scrapes and Bruises

Where you stumble, there lies your treasure.
—Joseph Campbell

L ooking back now, we realize that our childhoods were filled with moments of unsupervised exploration inside and outside of school hours. It seemed everyone ran with a motley crew of latchkey kids and quasi-delinquents. This was literally a recipe for some kind of physical disaster or endangerment, which rarely factored into whether to attempt some of the aforementioned childhood stunts involving running, jumping, biking, rolling, tumbling, or swinging. You just did it. Consequences came later, and they were, for the most part, a relatively inexpensive price to pay for risky behavior. Fearlessness came preinstalled for Gen Xers and baby boomers.

I (Sunil) remember something called "The Adventure Playground" at our school. Built around the time I was in the fourth grade, it was pure, state-of-the-art danger! Concrete tunnels. Rickety wooden bridges. Single-log walking structures. In 1973, that's how playgrounds were built. I distinctly remember a water slide park in downtown Toronto being built with concrete as well. You slid down the thing with a rubber mat! If you fell off your mat, which happened quite often, you were a prime candidate for some serious scrapes, all while screaming "*wheeeeeeeee*" down the slide.

Boy, oh boy, did we get hurt in the 1970s. That was the cost of play. You were going to incur some nicks, cuts, and bruises. We had no clue that all the edgy play, risk-taking, and hard knocks were strongly shaping who we were and teaching us mental and physical freedom. While I am sure you are nodding in agreement, you might be dismissing that time as "the good old days," which are not possible to recreate.

Guess what? Bruce McLachlan, a principal at Swanson Primary School in Auckland, New Zealand, has brought back those halcyon days of Evel Knievel recklessness and then some! Not only do parts of his school's playground resemble a construction site; there are absolutely no playground rules. That's right. No rules.

Here is the opening paragraph from an article on the playground that in appeared in *The Atlantic* in 2014:

> There are no rules on the playground at Swanson Primary School in Auckland, New Zealand. Students are allowed to climb trees, ride skateboards, and play contact games. This relaxed approach to playtime started as a research experiment conducted by two local universities, but it went so well that the school opted to make the changes permanent. According to a recent article, the school "is actually seeing a drop in bullying, serious injuries, and vandalism, while concentration levels in class are increasing.

How about we map teaching mathematics on these kinds of obstacles and hurdles and give students the freedom, space, and curiosity to stumble while *smiling*? Jo Boaler would call this *celebrating struggle*. This nice sketchnote that she posted on Twitter whimsically captures the power of her celebrated Growth Mindset.

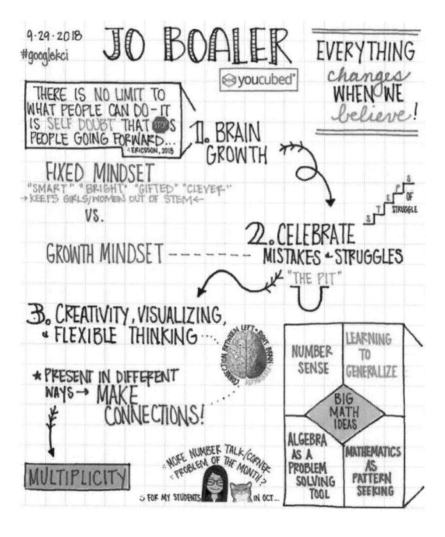

Without struggle, you cheapen the mathematical experience at best. At worst, you set students up for anxiety and frustration when they cannot solve problems that are not like those they have seen in textbooks or practiced dozens of times—when they cannot solve a problem in the time it takes to boil an egg. Struggling is the gateway not only to patience—which is not simply the ability to wait *but to have a constructive attitude while waiting*—but also to the long game of adding value and purpose to our lives.

If it sounds too simple, maybe we have complicated math education to the point where the mathematics content is sometimes buried beneath pedagogy, well intentioned as it might be. How about just giving kids damn good math problems and getting the hell out of their way? A decent definition of "good" would be that even if students did not get the question right or got stuck at some point, they would *still* give the questions a thumbs up! Now repeat. Forever. This is the true measure of learning and understanding mathematics for students and teachers too.

The correctness should have little currency, if any, to the value of the math problem. Students are starving for rich mathematical problems that line up with their curiosities and skills and innate desire to be challenged. This is more than a strong hunch. This is a scientific fact.

In 1975 Mihaly Csikszentmihalyi came up with his concept of "flow," a zone where people can maximize their individual skills to be in a state of constant euphoria and, specifically, a place of *optimal experience*. The image that follows shows various regions where skills and challenges can meet.

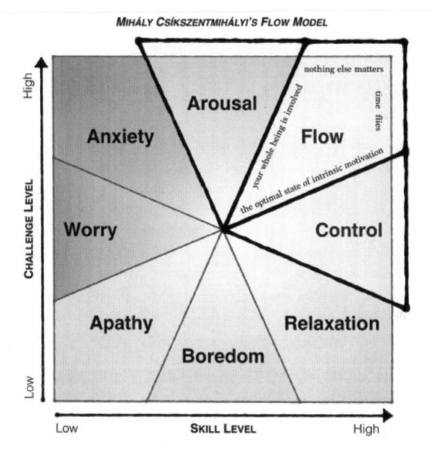

MIHÁLY CSÍKSZENTMIHÁLYI'S FLOW MODEL

Most of the zones should be familiar to all of us. Anxiety, worry, apathy, and boredom have been historical reactions by millions of disenfranchised math students. Each and every one of those students, however, has the capability of achieving the flow state, or, at the very least, the surrounding regions of arousal and control. It just depends on knowing the capabilities of all our students and selecting math problems with maximum challenge and fun. It is here we find educational gold—the optimal state of intrinsic motivation, which fuels the journey that is mathematics.

A true love for mathematics by students in schools has generally been absent. Maybe the word *dormant* is a better choice, because the potential to be in mathematical flow has always been there. It is just that there have been long-standing academic and social barriers. We all agree that math questions that embody the *low-floor and high-ceiling* approach have the best results in large student engagement. What about starting with prime numbers, the basic building blocks of all numbers? And don't tell students what they are. Let them, for the love of all things *experiential*, discover it for themselves! We are in recess mode, right? A good and addictive game to play before and after this activity is the "Is It Prime?" game. Numbers appear as soon as you hit "Start," and you have to select whether the number is prime. If you get it wrong, the game is over. If you get it right, another number appears. The game continues until you get one wrong or sixty seconds elapses. It's a brilliant way to build automaticity in recalling prime numbers. It has great replay value—an important criterion for any math game!

isthisprime.com/game

Activity 2

Get kids into groups of 4/5 and give them each group about 100 of those Unifix Cubes. Ask kids to make towers from 1 to 10. Instruct the kids to examine which towers cannot be made into a different rectangle or square.

The ones that cannot be are called Prime Numbers.

Have kids find Prime Numbers up to 30!

When we were taught math, numbers had no color or personality—hence the army-like saying of being "treated like a number." When numbers are poked and prodded, much like when kids poke their fingers into dirt, mud, or slime to engage with the texture and feel of these inviting substances, the details and *personalities* of numbers emerge.

The gulf between students just seeing numbers as being aesthetically equal and having no unique characteristics and students discovering the rich patterns and connections that numbers are screaming to share is currently unbridgeable. At a very young age, children should discover what a prime number is and how there doesn't seem to be a recognizable pattern to their occurrence. My own kids, who are currently in middle school, know their primes from 2 to 223. I was content to stop at 97, but *they wanted* to continue. Happy sigh!

You can then tell them that it is mathematics' greatest secret, and the person who unlocks it will become one of the most famous people to have ever lived. How is that for adding a bit of drama and intrigue to Monday morning math class?

In all seriousness, simple activities such as prime number play have the power to connect your students to some of the deepest probes of the mathematical universe. Such a connection makes it far more likely that young people will maintain that exploration throughout their lives. Finding joy in mathematical discovery at a young age is the best chance we have to ensure a lifetime of mathematical exploration. But we must act early, making sure to present students with math questions and problems that spark curiosity, are fun to solve, and lead to even more questions.

Here is a question I (Sunil) posted on Twitter from my first book. In a few days, it sparked a wonderful conversation on social media:

Sunil Singh
@Mathgarden

This is the problem I gave all my students the first week back...it's a great activity to sharpen arithmetic skills, class collaboration, and test resilience...:) It was one of the "Magnificent Seven" problems I put in my book Pi of Life: The Hidden Happiness of Mathematics.

SEVEN 89

THE 24 PROBLEM

Put the numbers 1 to 24 down the left-hand side of a piece of paper. On the top, put the numbers 1, 3, 4, and 6. Underneath these key numbers put the operations of +, −, ×, and ÷. The task is to create questions that give the answers for all the numbers from 1 to 24. There are no restrictions on the operations (you can use whichever ones you want as often as you need them). However, you must use each of the numbers 1, 3, 4, and 6 exactly once. And, there can be no concatenation—i.e., you can't construct a "13" by putting the 1 and 3 together.

Here are some of the answers for the first few numbers.

$$1 = (6 - 3) \div (4 - 1)$$
$$2 = (3 + 1) \div (6 - 4)$$
$$3 = (6 - 4 - 1) \times 3$$
$$4 = 6 + 3 - 4 - 1$$

There were so many great responses. Here are a few.

 Glenn Waddell, Jr. @gwaddellnvhs · 15h

My learners have been stuck on 24 for two days, and have told me to go away! They want to figure it out for themselves! Love it so much. They are angry with me for even suggesting I could help them. <3 <3 @NevadaTeach #pretchat @Mathgarden

 Glenn Waddell, Jr. @gwaddellnvhs

Thank you @Mathgarden for the problem yesterday. I gave it to my college students to play with this morning. Let's see what they do! #mtbos #Iteachmath @NevadaTeach

 Nico Rowinsky @rowmath · 5 Sep 2018

Happening today. Use 1,3,4 and 6 in any combination to get a result of 1 to 24. Thanks @Mathgarden for the idea.

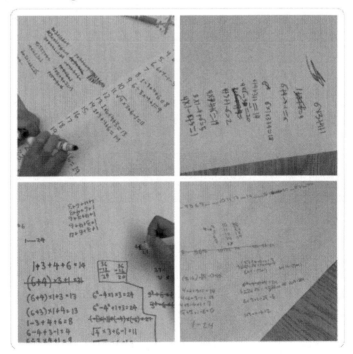

The "24 problem" was my first day/first week question for more than ten years. Students got to practice their PEDMAS (parenthesis, exponents, multiplication, division, addition, subtraction) operations with a reverse twist, and lying in wait for them at the end was one of the greatest gifts of doing mathematics—resilience. The sooner they saw proof of their own resilience, the more willing they were to tackle more challenging math questions! Enchantment and frustration often go hand in hand in mathematics. We should not try to separate the two! [Can't you just feel SMP: 1 all up in here? Also 2, 3, and 7]

The learning and *appreciation* of something like prime numbers—after all, math is an art form—must occur early on. It just has to. It becomes the foundation of wanting to play with numbers, which is why the "24 problem" is so gripping and fascinating. *Wanting* to play with numbers leads to arithmetic—which is, of course, the gateway to all mathematics! The fascination that my kids have with primes was primarily fueled by playing the award-winning game, *Prime Climb*. This game, I believe, is one of the main reasons my kids enjoy multiplying and dividing in their heads.

The creator of the game, Dan Finkel, has a TEDx Talk out of Seattle (which now is housed in the official TED Talk site) that speaks to the wonderful patterns found on the game board and the critical elements of outstanding mathematical teaching. It is now one of the most watched TEDx Talks on mathematics.

"Five Principles of Extraordinary Math Teaching," Dan Finkel, TEDxRainier
bit.do/mathrecess2

The Fifty Game

At the beginning of this book, The Sweet Sound of Disruption, the Fifty Game was referenced as inducing absolute pandemonium in a fourth-grade classroom in the Bronx. The laughing and screaming occurred because of the students' *repeated failure* to discover the hidden pattern and strategy needed to win the game. Despite the failure, there was no loss of excitement to keep playing the game.

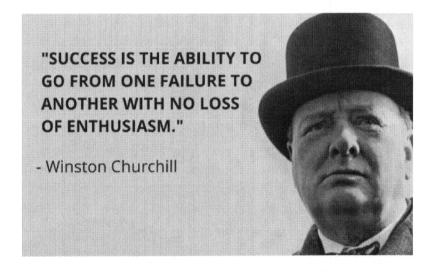

"SUCCESS IS THE ABILITY TO GO FROM ONE FAILURE TO ANOTHER WITH NO LOSS OF ENTHUSIASM."

- Winston Churchill

The game starts by writing the number 50 on the board. A student volunteer is chosen, and the instructions are simple. The teacher and student will take turns subtracting numbers. Think of it as fifty cards, and the repeated removal of cards. When there is one card left, whoever's turn it is, is the loser. The key rule is that you *cannot remove more than half the cards remaining at any time*. That means you cannot remove 49 from 50 and leave your opponent with 1 and declare yourself the winner. The largest number of cards that can be removed is twenty-five. Below are some possible game situations:

50 40 38 20 10 9 7 4 3 2 1
50 27 24 15 12 6 3 2 1
50 47 40 20 18 10 7 4 3 2 1
50 30 15 7 5 3 2 1

As you can see, at no time were more than half of the cards removed. Students tend to catch on quickly to that, and they have a *funstrating* time trying to figure out how to win!

As with Sprouts, there is an optimal way of playing. The person who goes first will always win, even when both opponents know the winning strategy. The winning strategy can best be described as thinking backwards—one of the most valuable strategies in the toolbox of mathematical thinking—about the "danger numbers" or the numbers you don't want to end up on!

One is a danger number because it signals the end of the game. What is the next danger number? Keeping in mind the critical rule of not being able to remove more than half, the next danger number is three. The next one is seven. Do you see the pattern?

1 3 7 15 31 63 127 255 511 1023 2047

It doesn't matter what number you start with. It could be 992130001. As long you go first and remove enough to take your opponent down to 2^n-1. This game was played with elementary kids, and its rich patterning is embedded with high school recursion and exponents. Even after two full boards of student losses, the collective perseverance of the classroom only amplifies. The more intense the failure, the more intense the effort. The Fifty Game needs its own first aid box! [SMP: 7, 1, and 3]

Prime Factorization Headache

Most of the time, students learn about prime factorization in middle school. (Though it's somewhat beside the point, prime factorization actually could be learned earlier if primes and composites were learned much earlier.) Most experiences with this topic simply involve starting with any composite number and asking students to break it down by exhausting divisibility by 2, 3, 7, etc. (If you can identify a prime number, you can easily identify a composite number. All you do is look at all the other whole numbers. In other words, composite numbers are all the whole numbers that are evenly divisible by numbers other than themselves and one. Fifteen is an example because both 3 and 5 divide evenly into 15. Fifteen is not a prime, which means it is composite.) While there is merit to doing these tasks, there isn't much going on here that is going to test the resilience of students.

Aided by a calculator and a list of primes, every student will be able to break down a number, let's say 10,296, into 2 × 2 × 2 × 3 × 3 × 11 × 13. What they would do is try dividing by 2 first. This would yield 5,198. They would try dividing by 2 again. Now they are down to 2,699. At this point, they could try 2 again—no harm in that—but there is no more divisibility by 2 left! At this point, they would move on to 3 and keep trying primes in order until they did not work. Take a look at how the finished prime factorization would look like—inside a playful stocking.

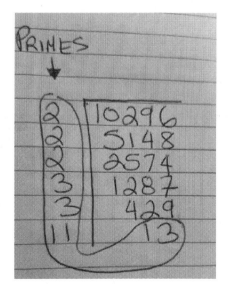

After a while, these become tedious, and like so many worksheet questions, obligatory, but what if instead of taking a flat prime factorization path, we asked our students to go *rock climbing* with this topic instead?

A few years ago, I (Sunil) was a regular contributor to *The New York Times*' Numberplay section, writing about a particular puzzle every four months or so. In spring 2017, I wrote about a puzzle that I received from Sam Vandervelde of The Proof School in San Francisco. Here's the excerpt from my column:

> Last spring, I was in San Francisco for the 94th annual National Council of Teachers of Mathematics Conference. One of the many people I had the pleasure of meeting was Sam Vandervelde of The Proof School. Before our meeting, I had sent him some puzzles and problems covering various aspects of mathematics. In the spirit of giving, Sam gave me this wonderful chestnut, that he himself was given. Here is the actual problem in Sam's words:
>
> > *Imagine that at a talk you write a colossally large number on the board. Then you number all the attendees from 1 to 200 and ask each of them in turn whether your huge number is divisible by their number. (So attendee #153 has to answer whether your number is divisible by 153, and so on for all 200 people in the audience.) Suppose further that everyone answers "YES" and that in fact only two people get the question wrong. If those two people are adjacent, then what are their numbers?*
> >
> > *Have fun sleuthing and unpacking this gem of a puzzle!*
> >
> > *Thank you, Sunil!*

In the spirit of celebrating different problem-solving strategies, let's start with a *smaller* room of twenty people. A simpler case. As is critical to the solution of the original problem, the numbers 1 to 20 are broken down to their prime factors if they are not prime themselves.

1	$6 = 2 \times 3$	11	$16 = 2 \times 2 \times 2 \times 2$
2	7	$12 = 2 \times 2 \times 3$	*17*
3	$8 = 2 \times 2 \times 2$	*13*	$18 = 2 \times 3 \times 3$
$4 = 2 \times 2$	$9 = 3 \times 3$	$14 = 2 \times 7$	*19*
5	$10 = 2 \times 5$	$15 = 3 \times 5$	$20 = 2 \times 2 \times 5$

Let's say we write the number 4,564,560 on the board. Are there any seat numbers who are not factors of this number? How about we break down this number into its prime factors: $2 \times 2 \times 2 \times 2 \times 3 \times 5 \times 7 \times 11 \times 13 \times 19$. On closer examination, it seems that there is no 17 and, because there is only one three, the number 9 is also not a factor of this this seven-digit number. It demands two 3s!

For this particular problem, though, you are not going to break down this really large number for the simple reason you do not know this really large number! Use your imagination and envision that it is broken down into all its prime components—and how many there are of each of them. Now there are two people, sitting side by side among seats numbered 1 to 200, who are not factors of this large number. What are they? [SMP: 1, 2, 6, 7, 8]

Here's the solution:

> It is easy to imagine that one of the seats must be prime. It is not easy to imagine that this even number is also one of the seats! Why this one? What makes it so special? Maybe we should examine some wrong answers! First, the two seats are not between 1 and 100. Let's say you guess the numbers as 59 and 60. Are you saying that 120 is a factor—which is simply multiplying by 2 (which is a factor)? If 60 wasn't a factor, then neither could be any multiple of it. Remember that only these two seat numbers are the odd ones out. Every other seat from 1 to 200 apparently divides into this large number. The answer lies in the number 2. It is the smallest prime number. What number has the most number of 2s below 200? That would be 128, which is $2 \times 2 \times 2 \times 2 \times 2 \times 2 \times 2$. No other number will "demand" this many 2s! And sitting right next to it is the number 127, which is prime!

Take a breath. There has been some soreness and head throbbing that has been woven into the math problems in this chapter. Do you know what else has been subtly threaded in here? Base 2. It popped up in the Fifty Game, and it is a consideration in the puzzle above. Our point is that instead of merely teaching exponent rules, try inserting them into problems so that the theories of mathematics can also be experienced as a product of the problem or application. That's right. Let's do a reverse and discuss mathematical theory second, *not first*.

Keeping with that theme, and the idea of base 2, here is another problem that is rather difficult but will spark many different strategies, lots of trial and error, and passionate discussion among your students.

Scrambled Eggs

There is a somewhat classic problem that has floated around the internet. It involves dropping eggs from different floors of a building. There is always something fun, a tad mischievous about dropping things out of a building. When I was in the sixth grade, we had a class trip to Canada's capital of Ottawa. When we checked into our room, which was on the fifth floor, there was an unopened box of Kraft dinner. It took us all of thirty seconds or so to dump the macaroni out the window. Oh those wacky '70s. Unsupervised kids acting like amateur rock stars. Dropping eggs, even in a math problem, sounds pretty enticing!

We are going to adjust the question for the purposes of this chapter. The simplest way to explain this problem is to start with one egg. There is a 128-story building. Your job is to figure out the highest floor from which the egg can be dropped and not break. Some kids would naturally go right to the 128th floor. They could get lucky, and their eggs might not break, but what if they do? Then you have failed at answering the question. Most students realize they have to start at the first floor and go up floor by floor until they reach the breaking point. The harder question involves solving this problem with two eggs. In fact, the solution involves a quadratic inequality equation. That's cool but a little advanced right now! Let's give students an infinite supply of eggs, and let's see if they can come up with a strategy that uses the fewest eggs—definitely fewer than 128 eggs! Maybe you can see why we chose 128 floors.

Here is the link to the best article and discussion of the egg and building problem: datagenetics.com/blog/july22012/index.html.

Happy Birthday!

It is unfortunate that the only base most kids learn is base ten. Of course kids should learn about base ten—just look at our fingers and toes! What if we had a different number of them? What would our arithmetic look like? What would our world look like? We certainly wouldn't be celebrating milestones that always end in zero! After base ten, as has been implicitly and explicitly stated in this chapter, base two is the most obvious and critical base to learn. It is binary and related to coding, but there is this natural fascination by kids to double. 1, 2, 4, 8, 16, 32, 64, 128, 256, 512, 1,024, 2,048, 4,096, 8,192, 16,384, 32,758, 65,516, 131,032, etc.

The reason I went to 131,032 is that is the number that my son, Aidan, had learned his "doubles" to when he was in fourth grade. He didn't memorize them. *We* figured out each one along the way! Doubling was not only fun, it was a rapid catapulting into higher numbers he might not have encountered—*and wanted to encounter*—otherwise. This also paved the way for the necessity to explain exponents to him. Waiting to teach exponents when it is expected in the curriculum usually siphons out any magic or curiosity. Giving it to students at grade levels *much lower* is in their wheelhouse of rigor and imagination. They will see and appreciate the "compactness" of exponents. It just opens more doors to more exploration, and some of those doors are really, really monstrous! We will discuss some of these in Chapter 7.

Another base two problem that causes students much bewilderment and bemusement is the birthday problem. It's actually not a problem. It's actually some clever mathematical trickery involving binary numbers and our birth dates, numbers from 1 to 31. Students are asked to look at the cards below. For added fun, just share the image below on a data projector. Because you will know the birthdays of your students, ask them to think of any number from one to thirty-one. When I (Sunil) go to classroom, I am a guest speaker, so I can easily use birthdays!

Card 4	Card 3	Card 2	Card 1	Card 0
16 17 18 19	8 9 10 11	4 5 6 7	2 3 6 7	1 3 5 7
20 21 22 23	12 13 14 15	12 13 14 15	10 11 14 15	9 11 13 15
24 25 26 27	24 25 26 27	20 21 22 23	18 19 22 23	17 19 21 23
28 29 30 31	28 29 30 31	28 29 30 31	26 27 30 31	25 27 29 31

Students are asked to examine the cards and look for their birth date and tell me all the cards they found it on. If a student was born on the 27th, they would find that number in Card 4, Card 3, Card 1, and Card 0. Just seconds after they tell me their last card, I have the answer in my head! Look at the top left number in each box—16, 8, 4, 2, and 1, the binary numbers. You simply add up these numbers! So for the example, the total would be 16 + 8 + 2 + 1 (they didn't point to Card 3). An element you could add here is for kids to create their own cards! Start right at the beginning by asking kids to write the numbers 1 to 31 on a piece of paper and get sums for each of them just using the doubling numbers—no more than once!

    1 = 1
    2 = 2
    3 = 1 + 2
    4 = 4
    5 = 1 + 4
    And so on...

Then students can organize all the numbers that contained a 1 in one box, a 2 in another, and all the way to 16. By completing this activity, students will feel they had greater ownership of the magic trick and deeper understanding of the mathematics behind it. Funny

how ownership and understanding are so closely linked together!
[SMP: 8, 7, 1]

The Josephus Problem

The final problem in this chapter is one of my favorites because it weaves in elements of math history, fundamentals of problem solving, and of course, something to do with base two in the solution.

The original problem dates back to the first century and a Jewish historian named Flavius Josephus, who, along with forty other soldiers, was trapped by Roman soldiers in a cave. The actual problem involves murder, so for our purposes, we will adjust the problem and lighten it up a bit!

Let's pretend there are forty-one kids in a circle. Each is armed with, I don't know, a cream pie. They will have to throw a cream pie at the person standing immediately to their left, and then that person will be out. Then the person immediately next to the person who just got hit will do the same. This whole *pie-throwing-to-the-immediate-left* will continue until there is only one kid left holding a cream pie.

The question is, if there are 41 students armed with pies, where should you stand to survive the game? Let's go back to the try-a-simpler-problem strategy! It will also help us understand how this puzzle works.

Take a look at the numbers above. One will throw a pie at two. Two is gone. Three will throw a pie at four. Four is gone. Five will throw a pie at six. Six is gone. These will be the people left after one round of pie-throwing:

At this point, it is seven's turn, which will lead us into round two. Seven will hit one. Three will hit five. And lastly, seven will get the last throw of the pie, and hit three. So, with a group of seven people, the winning position is seven. But the suggestion should be to start with two people and record the winning position. You could actually draw a diagram with forty-one positions and start slashing people, but there is a very cool pattern that can be seen well before that! [SMP: 1 and 3 are big here, and making sense of this problem requires making a good argument for the sense you make.]

The Josephus Problem, Numberphile
bit.do/mathrecess4

When kids play, they play hard. We all played hard as kids. I think we are hard-wired for being curious risk-takers. It's probably in our DNA. Fearlessness is a natural byproduct. The occasional wipeout is a temporary setback, if that even. There is no differentiation between success and failure—they are bundled and braided inextricably. This is play. There is a myth that if it is play, then it can't be rigorous. Last time I checked, rock climbing was pretty darn hard!

Mathematics. Let's play hard. Let's download delightful challenges onto our elementary kids. Not because we are trying to meet higher academic standards, but because we are trying to meet higher *play* standards. Not through boring worksheets or repetitive drills. Through challenging problems. We purposely chose base two problems to build up these *math calluses*. That is because after base ten, it is the one that kids naturally gravitate toward—the doubling numbers, 2, 4, 8, 16, 32, 64, 128, etc.

While we are strongly advocating for children being exposed to playful mathematics that is inherently complex, we also are recommending that we assess children in highly progressive and creative ways that are simpatico with such dense problem-solving. We need to be just as disruptive in our evaluation of students.

QUESTIONS FOR DEEPER DISCUSSION

1. Try out the Birthday Problem. Print out some cards like those here and baffle your students with your ability to know their birth dates. Guide them through the process of making the cards and learning the trick. This might take some time, but you will be building a strong sense of how numbers can be formed using the powers of two.

2. The title of this chapter, "Scrapes and Bruises," was chosen because we have had to work hard at understanding these concepts. They were not obvious to us at first either. How can you play with some of the ideas in this chapter and explore them with your students? Don't be afraid to get your own scrapes and bruises!

3. Play the Josephus game in a circle with lots of kids, several times, each time with a different number of students, and watch as they form conjectures. Be sure to test them, reject them, and learn!

CHAPTER 3

Grades Are
for Onions

You may say I am a dreamer...

—John Lennon

Pardon me, I (Chris) have to get out some bandages and Tylenol after Chapter 2, but what a glorious bit of scuffing about in mathematics!

Another thing Sunil and I share, despite growing up in disparate time zones and being separated by a few years, is a love of '70s and '80s music. All the good music. In this chapter, I take inspiration from John Lennon's "Imagine," a classic tune that continues to ring true through the ages.

"Imagine there's no heaven. … Imagine all the people living for today. …"

Let's take a little wander into an education world that truly values playfulness, experimentation, and accomplishment over assessment, labels, and separating the good from the not so good. I wrote a blog post a while back—it might be the post that confirmed to Sunil that we could work together on a book. I started it with a story that I'd like to relate here in more detail. Along the way, I will also make a case for some major disruption in the status quo of schools.

In late spring 1982, I was twenty-one, newly married, and broke. I had completed only three semesters of community college studies, and I was searching for my grand purpose in life. A friend of mine was a farmer in the Central Valley of California, where he grew onions and melons. He told me that there was money to be made working for him in the onion fields. It was minimum wage, but he said the hours would be long through the summer, and I could earn a lot of money—enough to afford to return to school in the fall. I took a job working in a packing shed that leased land and grew onions and other vegetables. My task, no experience needed, was to walk row upon row of harvested onions, counting burlap sacks filled with two 5-gallon buckets of onions. Within a few days, I was ecstatic to learn I had been promoted to "onion grader." (At first, I thought the job was onion *grater*!) The onion grader was quite a machine, and one, I came to learn, that had shade.

About a dozen of us would stand around the grader, which was hauled by a tractor. The purpose of this machine was to separate the onions by size (a type of grade) and fill market-ready bags. The skilled workers in this crew were the women who could, by touch, assess the colossal-grade onions and put them into the proper bags. All other grades of onions were found by ever larger grates on the conveyor that drove onions past hands, and into the market bags. For the most part, my work was to pull out the rotten onions and toss them over the side of the machine. This went on for twelve hours a day, and it was grueling, dusty, hot work but less miserable than what I was doing before. The image of that work fills my mind whenever I am asked to assign a grade to a student. It is a miserable experience, grueling, with vision obscured by bias, and, at times, tear inducing.

Sunil and I have a collection of Mutual Math Friends (MMFs), and one of them is Dr. Matthew Beyrenevand from Massachusetts. The blog post I mention here was spurred on by an excellent one by Matthew called "Retaking Assessments: Many Math Teachers Are Late to the Party!" He advocates that math teachers need to embrace the practice of retaking assessments and that the "one chance only" mindset that is often present in classrooms is harmful and contrary to what we know about learning. His post got me thinking about onions for some reason, specifically about sorting onions. You see, it matters in that industry that we separate colossal onions from large, medium, and small ones; each has its own terminus in the marketplace of onions. The question I struggle with as a teaching professor is, do I want to view my students like those onions?

"...but I'm not the only one..."

A colleague in Canada, Dave Martin, President of MCATA (Mathematics Council of the Alberta Teachers Association), has written anecdotally about his experiences in abolishing grades in his classes. Furthermore, he goes on to describe the process he uses instead. Students are challenged, they argue, and they present their findings. Retention is up; understanding is as well. And this is in calculus courses, notoriously high in attrition and lack of understanding. Read his full blog postings here:

403
bit.do/mathrecess-dmartin

As a professor of mathematics in Canada, he has written several blogs about how he has given up grades in his calculus classes. He was confronting the issue of changing the culture of calculus courses from being a "weeding out" of students to a welcoming space where all students can learn calculus. (It's my opinion that the long-used and widespread metaphor that refers to learners as produce is misguided.) It seems that as soon as David switched to an assessed but nongraded system, his retention rates went up, as did the commensurate success in the course. This is a common response, and lest you think this means a lowering of standards, most teachers in ungraded settings report a rise in understanding.

What good is gained in assigning a grade to a child's work? The concept of 90–100 percent equals an A, 80–89 percent equals a B, and so on, is subjective and fraught with fallacy. Because a child can do every question on an arbitrarily selected and constructed exam—and do so by anticipating what it is you are looking for with 100 percent accuracy—does not mean they understand or can explain what the mathematics is about. Who created these standards? And why?

Those who advocate "normalizing" and "curving" the process are even more subjective and, quite honestly, cruel. The practice of insisting on class performance always falling within a forced curve-fitting exercise is both stupid and downright mean. As a first counter to that argument, shouldn't I, the teacher, want and expect that every child succeeds in my class? Every single one? I am not arguing that they will, just that they all have that opportunity. If you are a teacher who "grades on the curve," you are predetermining that a fixed portion of your students will have to fail. The goal of this process is to ensure that roughly two-thirds of all students are within a single standard deviation of the average score; then from there establish "cut-scores" that delineate Cs from Bs, As, Ds, and Fs. (Students, don't kid yourselves. Never ask your teacher or professor to "curve" the scoring on your exam.) This practice replaces a system of learning that should be inherently social and collaborative with the isolating crush of competition. You end up competing not with the subject's standard or criteria but with your fellow students. I urge teachers and students alike to rise up and revolt against the bell curve in grading! Then eliminate the idea of grades altogether.

What alternatives are there to traditional grades?

One of my ideas is to have students create a portfolio of their work in a specific unit of study. Students would curate a collection of demonstrations of techniques and skills and put them on display—digitally or in print—similar to a résumé or CV. In this era of practically unlimited data storage, this could easily be accomplished. Each student would need to not only think broadly about themselves and their accomplishments but be able to tailor their public images for particular needs (e.g., when applying for that entry-level data entry job, you provide evidence of your keyboarding skills, but when you are applying for the job as an auto body worker, you present before-and-after photos of your work.)

What about applying to a university or college? A layered and diverse digital portfolio will easily suffice. A student needs only to submit a thorough collection of their work in high school—writing samples, PowerPoints of history projects, Google Slides of completed math problems, and videos of oral presentations from virtually any course of study. University and college admission officials already ask students to provide nongraded materials such as proof of community service, musical performance recordings, and records of sports accomplishments.

Back to Why Not?

Should our children be assigned an arbitrary grade much like we use for factory-produced vegetables? Grading is an anachronistic holdover from the scientific management era, inserted into schooling during the nineteenth century. Performance serves as a proxy for comprehension and the ability to coherently discuss or deploy reasoning. In a later chapter, I will explore this idea, looking specifically at how many educators in Finland are approaching the task of assessing student learning.

Grades in Finnish schools are nothing like those generated in the United States. Finnish educators have moved their students focus off of generating a score on a test to actual learning and demonstration of that learning. One way they do this is by postponing all formal, norm-referenced, and standardized exams until children are ready to graduate secondary school.

Do not kid yourself into believing that the grading system isn't about grading the children. Think about how adults describe themselves decades after their school days are over—"I was an A student" and "Pay no attention to me; I was a C student." Children know that the grades they receive are marks on them as people, not their product. Those grades can be both overinflating, and depressingly deflating.

Warning! The next section gets a little academic—it's the researcher in me.

Schneider and Hutt (2013) provide an excellent history of how the grading system took hold in the United States, tracing its history into the early nineteenth century. This practice began in the Ivy League colleges and was patterned after European colleges, specifically Prussian schools. These schools placed heavy emphasis on competitive assignments and identifying the highest-achieving students to separate them from the rest. Horace Mann, for all the wonderful things he brought to American Common Schools, was instrumental in the creation of our graded system.

In answer to some of the early criticisms of the competition model, Mann advocated a system of graded classrooms from first grade to eighth grade. These would allow students to be "re-ranked" annually rather than once at the end of their schooling years. It still sounds competitive to me, but I'm no Horace Mann, right? The education reformers of the day likened grading to an accountant's ledger. Emphasizing the accumulation of successes (no record of nonsuccesses) for purposes of determining, and reporting, "in a compendious manner, the punctuality, deportment, and comparative merit of the pupil, in his recitations…"

By the mid-nineteenth century, there were already some concerns being raised with this antimoral system of ranking students against each other. Why is ranking an important outcome of education? Do we need to know who is best or worst at reading the minds of their teachers and regurgitating what those teachers want? In a recent speech, Dr. Diane Ravitch, an education researcher and former assistant secretary of education in the admin-

Diane Ravitch blog post
bit.do/mathrecess-DRavitchBlog

istration of President George H.W. Bush, made the point that we have built for ourselves an education system predicated on winners and losers with a high need for accounting of outcomes.

My point in this is that we seem to have forgotten that learning is our purpose. The goal of growing humans into their best selves is no longer central to our endeavor. If learning is about finding your best happiness, how will that occur if students are constantly worrying about whether they get an A or avoid an F? Where does learning fit inside a grading system predicated on a so-called "normal distribution" of outcomes? If some have to get As, some must also have to get Fs, and the overwhelming majority who get Bs to Ds get left out of focus.

I say the American system of education needs to drop its focus on grades as being the product of thirteen years of a child's life. Bring back to schooling the joy of learning because it will go farther than the negative consequences associated with grades. Our children are not onions.

But what are we to do until such a time that society is ready for a nongraded, performance-demonstrated means of reporting assessments of student learning? Note here the focus of student learning. Dave Martin's story, detailed in a series of blog posts on *Medium* in the Q.E.D. group of publications, might provide some important insight about moving toward this goal. Dave began by determining the core concepts from within his curriculum and focusing his assessments on these as outcomes. He describes how he would teach "2 or 3 outcomes at a level ..." he had identified as mastery, then provide an assessment written around those outcomes, which would test only the basics of the outcome. Nothing tricky added here; his assessment (not including commentary-like feedback) boiled down to "outcome demonstrated" or "needs to learn." Students who still need to learn are prescribed assistive actions, including a conversation with the teacher, followed by another assessment. No deductions are made for multiple attempts to learn.

After several outcomes are taught, an open project is assigned, which can be completed collaboratively but must be submitted individually. These projects are assessed in the same manner as individual outcomes as stated previously. Final grades for the course are created through a mathematical model that weights the projects twice as much as individual outcomes, to increase their effect on total score, and out pops a quantity that can be interpreted as a grade.

This method focuses on student learning as the primary goal of schooling, which is a major shift. Grades are typically about behavior modification more than assessment of learning.

As a side note, let's think a little about multiplication for a moment. We in the West spend a great deal of time worrying about how our children learn to multiply, especially their basic single-digit multiplication facts. I can say this emphatically, as I have had Master of Arts students in STEM education attempt to persuade me that they only need to study the best way to teach children these facts. As if knowing, really just being able to regurgitate in a hurry, these facts will make some lifelong difference. When asked why this matters, teachers assure me that kids need this to do multidigit multiplication. I usually stifle a cry of "B*&^@#*T!" and then show them this little method of multiplication, sometimes called "Duplation-Mediation," but I prefer "Doubling and Halving." Let's multiply 24 by 35 in this method, which I claim only requires being able to double or cut quantities in half along with addition.

Notice that in calculating this product all I need is to be able to divide by 2 and multiply by 2. I also need to ignore the idea that half of 3 is 1½ , and be happy to write down 1 without the fractional part. I choose to divide the number written in the left column and double the number in the right column, though it does not matter which I choose so long as I keep that practice throughout this problem. I continue the process of halving and doubling until the halving column has a 1 in it. The addition is accomplished in the columns and performed left to right or right to left, whichever makes you happiest. As is our practice in Exploding Dots, we explode the results, and voila!

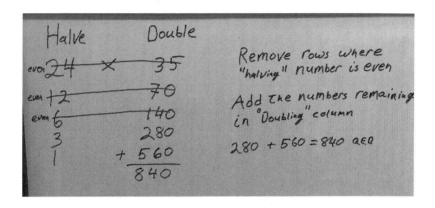

Let's try another one:

64 × 55

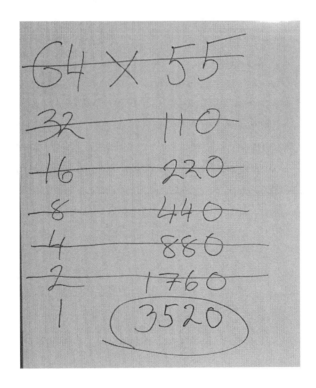

The reason this works is based entirely in the base-two system, which we looked at a little in Chapter 2 and is tantalizingly simple. If you know how the birthday guessing game works, that same principle is at play here. The secret is in the right-hand column, and the deep mystery is in why the "evens" in the left-hand column are removed. The reason for removing the rows with even numbers in the "halves" column is illustrated best in the second example. There we are looking to collect sixty-four 55s, and we only need the powers of 2 that either sum to 64 or exactly equal 64. We can drop out the even rows because they might, in fact, be adding two or zero of those powers of 2 into the mix. The odd rows give only a single value of the doubled number in that row. [SMP: 5, 6, 7]

To be clear, I show this method to my students to demonstrate that mindless regurgitation of single-digit multiplication facts is meaningless or minimally meaningful. If multiplication can be accomplished without ever referencing the facts through 12, why memorize them? Humans have produced myriad methods to accomplish this task, including the decomposition of the factors into primes or sums of powers of 10, etc. We are a creative species that will find ways to accomplish our counting tasks when confronted with proper motivation. The meaningless recitation of facts is not that motivation, and it has been shown to be counter motivational for many students. Let's seek a better way.

Back to grades. Why is it so important that kids get passing or failing grades depending on whether they can correctly multiply 9 by 6? It's not. The truth is, grades are for sorting, for separating good from better or bad, not for encouraging. These are not the labels that children need, and they are not productive within society. If it is not yet obvious, I have some deeply held goals for education, and labeling kids is not among them at all.

If you did not read the end of the Introduction where we talk about the Standards of Mathematical Practice, please do so now. These practices represent the larger goals of a mathematical education. Content standards, terms, and facts will come and go (less than one hundred years ago teachers needed to teach their students their *surds*, how to calculate one hundred weight and use trigonometric tables as part of their basic curriculum), but there are broader purposes that do not change. These broader purposes are also more challenging to assess, but they do lend themselves to being demonstrated in work-products of students. This is why I advocate for the electronic portfolio curated by the students themselves.

One overarching goal of mathematics education is to provide humans with the facility and confidence necessary to view their world with eyes wide open with both wonder and analysis. Our call for a math recess in this book is to simultaneously liberate the student and the subject they study. Memorization of factoids (which is all that knowing in an instant that $12 \times 11 = 132$) is not thinking, and it is not required to see the world of mathematics as a playground or as a way to see your world accurately. No grade of A, B, or C will ever accurately confirm this ability.

Mathematics education researchers Al Cuoco, E. Paul Goldenberg, and June Mark wrote an excellent document in 1996, which they titled "Habits of Mind: An Organizing Principle for Mathematics Curricula." It was forward-thinking for its time. In the opening paragraphs, they painted an alternative landscape to the present-day curricular focus on factoids, empty procedures, and results with "much more important than specific mathematical results are the habits of mind used by the people who create those results." This is further echoed in the wonderful TED Talk given by Conrad Wolfram about sixteen years later, when he called for an inversion of the curricular process from solving preformed equations that have no context to mathematizing the world through modeling, working the model to its mathematical and logical conclusion (often using machines to do the grunt work that people are likely to make mistakes on), and evaluating the results.

These habits of mind, this inverted curriculum, are also often characterized by play and iteration—in other words, recess. Think back to the recess of your childhood. Did you ever try to decipher where a tetherball was going to end up by watching its swing and predicting where to put your arm? Did you and your friends experiment with rules to games or team arrangements? If a toy you were playing with wore down, did you add to it or tinker with it to keep it working? Read *Calvin and Hobbes*, the classic comic strip series, and notice the recurrent theme of "Calvin Ball," a game in which Calvin is constantly inventing new rules. This was my experience as a child playing hide-and-seek.

The following goals for math students should permeate all classroom experiences in mathematics: helping students to be pattern sniffers, experimenters, describers, tinkerers, inventors, visualizers, and conjecturers. An education system that emphasizes authentic learning over grades could implement these goals. It would be an education system that values and measures a student's prowess and success the same way proud parents might when their young Itzhak Perlman-esque violinist performs on stage or their hockey phenom daughter cultivates an exceptional talent on the ice over time.

We don't need to treat our children like produce to prepare them for adult life. We need them to grow into self-confident, logical, fact-assessing, fully-human persons who are able to have a sense of joy and wonder about their world.

QUESTIONS FOR DEEPER DISCUSSION

1. Take some time and investigate what you mean by the As, Bs, Cs, Ds, and Fs you assign to your students' work. What criteria do you use? If you use anything other than the traditional ninety-to-one-hundred scale, what is it, and why do you use it?

2. What can you do today that would elevate learning over grading as the criteria for assessment?

3. Consider some of the avoidable inequities that are established and ossified by our current grading labels—above average, below average, failing, etc. How have you seen those labels affect your treatment of students? How have you seen them affect your students' learning, academic outlook, or behavior?

CHAPTER 4

Math Playground

Math is not a spectator sport. It's not a body of knowledge. It's not symbols on a page. It's something you play with, it's something you do.

—Keith Devlin

In 1972, completely unknown to me (Sunil) and thousands of other kids, I played in what was the world's first ball pit at a place that would revolutionize how kids would play all over the world—the famous Children's Village at Ontario Place in Toronto, Canada. British-born Eric McMillan was the designer of this dearly loved slice of summer fun for millions of kids. He went on to be known as the "father of soft play." That moniker might be a bit misleading, as I rarely escaped Children's Village without skinned knees or rope-burnt hands. Although traditional amusement parks focused on children passively consuming fun through rides, the design of McMillan's landmark park relied on the active energy and enthusiasm of children. There were play zones such as the "Punching Bag Forest" and

"King of the Mountain." Here is a link to a short video, narrated by Eric McMillan, which captures the spirit of that magical place:

Ontario Place, Children's Village
bit.do/mathrecess3

The Village relied on children's own drives to run and screom, to build things and knock them over, to perform and safely flirt with danger.

—Nathan Storring

Physical risk, when paired with intrinsic fun, creates a learning synergy that fuels curiosity and resilience. Mathematics should be learned and explored the same way. Not so much because of people like Eric McMillan or Bruce McLachlan—who are certainly play pioneers—but more so because the entire history of mathematics is built on *bumbling and fumbling.*

Sandbox Learning

In open-world gaming, a concept that involves creating video game worlds that have nonlinear exploration, gaming challenges can be played in any sequence, and their encounters will be different for each player. In linear gameplay, every player plays the exact same challenges in the exact same order. Hmmm. That last sentence sounds a lot like *dated* math instruction.

The largest open-world game is *No Man's Sky*, which has a mind-boggling 2^{64} or eighteen quintillion planets to explore. It would take approximately five billion years to explore all the planets. (Not sure if the designers of the game thought everything through, as Stephen Hawking predicted we have only one thousand years left on Earth before we will need to find another planet!) The massive scope of the game speaks to a future of gaming that needs to be mapped on how we learn mathematics—with or without technology. Mathematics must always be a playground that just keeps growing and growing and growing.

In this chapter, Chris and I are giving you a good starting pack of resources—albeit just a few *planets* or so—of cool math problems, games, puzzles, riddles, conundrums, books, websites, and apps. It's a collection you can add to and continue building into a never-ending sandbox of mathematics.

Pencil Games

There is a deliberate attempt here to list an old, reliable, and sometimes undervalued resource—the pencil—as the first resource for a foray onto a math playground. The doorways to what we hope will be a lifetime exploration of mathematics should be as wide as possible and accessible to all. The pencil represents much more. For me it is a necessary doodling tool to scribble and play with when working a problem. It is also a necessary and satisfying instrument to write out solutions, or as Lockhart calls them, "reason poems."

When employed by a skilled teacher, this technology allows kids to tinker, try, fail and try again. It builds fine motor skills, hand-eye coordination, critical thinking and creativity. Best of all, in a time of shrinking school funds, this technology is incredibly affordable. It's a pencil.

—Dustin Dwyer

These games can be used in classrooms by teachers with students to enhance strategic thinking, number sense, mental arithmetic, spatial reasoning, and a host of other critical thinking skills. Before you ponder where they fit your class best, play them all for yourself. Play them for fun while taking long rides in cars with your own children or spouse, at the dinner table with family and friends, at a bar over drinks with coworkers. Gain an appreciation for their ability to bring simple joys to you, and then introduce them to students. Remember this book has a goal of altering perceptions of math for everyone, all learners. We have used them in a variety of ways in classes, unit introductions, transitional activities, middle-of-the-day joyful mental action breaks, and after walking across the campus at recess and seeing a child sitting alone interventions. The possibilities are as limited as your creativity.

Sim

Need

- Two players
- Paper
- Pencil

- Two pencils or crayons of different colors
- Ruler (optional)

How to Play

- Draw six dots and connect all the dots with a pencil. Players take turns drawing over lines with their color.
- Force your opponent to complete a triangle in her or his color

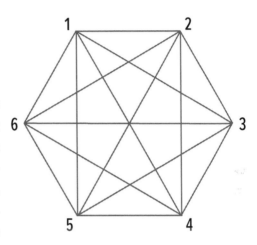

The first pencil game has a playing surface that resembles a hexagon and all the vertices connected with one another. Don't worry. The hexagon doesn't have to be perfect, and the lines themselves don't have to be super straight. You just need to have two pencils or crayons of different colors. You can skip the step of connecting all dots with a pencil and simply start the game with six dots and the same rules of play. Students take turns drawing over the lines with their color, ensuring that they never create a triangle with all of the sides having their color. Hence, the objective of the game—get your opponent to have a triangle with all sides in their color. We will revisit this game in the Chapter 7 as it is linked to something called *Ramsey Numbers* and one of the most incredible numbers in mathematics, Graham's Number! [SMP: 5, not so much about tools as being strategic, 1, and 8]

Nim

If you have not heard of the game Nim, you might think that it is some "twin variant" of the game Sim. It's not. As with Sim, there is a strategy to winning, but the strategy for winning Nim is easier to grasp. If Sim can be thought of as a game of adding lines, then Nim can be thought of as a game of subtracting objects—plastic counters are very popular. It's also just as easy to quickly draw circles.

Need

- Two Players
- Pencil and Paper

How to Play

- Players draw rows of circles
- Players take turns removing all or some of the circles from a particular row
- The last player to remove/cross out/erase the remaining circles/circle wins
- A good suggestion is to draw rows of five, seven, and nine circles. But you can have any number of rows and any number of circles in a row (1, 7, 11, or 16 would also be fine).

Strategy

- The strategy to win? We have been here before—base two!

Pencil and Paper Games, Nim
bit.do/mathrecess5

Board Games Closet

There are so many wonderful games that span the spectrum of mathematical thinking. We have categorized each game to help you decide which games you would like to explore!

A–Arithmetic Operations
C- Counting
D–Deductive Reasoning
G–Geometry
H–Math History
M–Memory
P–Patterning
S–Strategy
T–Time Element
V–Visual/Spatial Reasoning

There are four games that I always have in the house and take on road trips. They are Albert's Insomnia [SMP: 1, 2, 6, 7], Prime Climb [SMP: 1, 6, 7, 8], Yahtzee, and Set [SMP: 2, 3, 7]. These are games that are loved not only by me but by my two middle-school–aged kids. There are many stories to tell here as to how their love of mathematics has been woven inextricably through these foundational games. (We will unpack each of these games in detail in the next chapter.)

This list is courtesy of David Martin, President of the Mathematics Council of Alberta Teachers Association:

Tiny Polka Dot game (ASV)	Mancala (digital)(AS)
Prime Climb (AMPS)	Mölkky (A)
Shut the Box (AS)	Math Dice (A)
Ubongo (G)	Math Dice
Mobi (AS)	Chase (AT)
	Sumoku (AS)

Blokus (GSV)

Scotland Yard (S)

Puerto Rico (S)

Patchwork (C)

Quarto (SV)

Pylos (GSV)

Ticket to Ride (SV)

The Hare and the
Tortoise (CS)

Settlers of Catan (CGS)

Sleeping Queens (CM)

South of Sahara (AHPSV)

The Three Little Pigs (C)

Sequence (S)

Quixo (SV)

Quoridor (SV)

Santorini (SV)

Power Grid (S)

Liar's Dice (S)

Can't Stop

Connect 4 (digital)

Q bitz (S)

Yahtzee (digital) (ACS)

Tenzi (T)

Skip Bo (S)

Dominos (digital) (CS)

Chess (digital) (S)

Checkers (digital) (S)

Cribbage

Rummikub (PSV)

Snakes & Ladders (digital)

City of Zombies (ACS)

Albert's Insomnia (A)

Qwirkle (SV)

Logic Mazes

I cannot remember when or where I first discovered Robert Abbott's logic mazes. I believe I was searching for visual puzzles that would challenge my students—especially those that disliked traditional math. It is so far off the beaten path of what I was teaching. Abbott and his mazes are generally unknown to the educational community. Both of his books, *Mad Mazes* and *SuperMazes*, are out of print, but there might be copies on Amazon. The maze below is an adapted version that was first printed in 1962, the first of its kind. Care to guess where? Yup. A Martin Gardner article in *Scientific American*. Martin Gardner was such a giant in the world of recreational mathematics.

It is then of little surprise that we see his influence in most visual puzzles. The second maze is equally as frustrating. I use both in my Family Math Nights. It is one of the more popular stations.

> Travel along the roads from Start to Goal. At each intersection follow one of the arrows. That is, you can turn in a certain direction only when there is a curved line in that direction, and you can go straight only when there is a straight line. You can leave an intersection only at the head of an arrow. U-turns are not allowed.

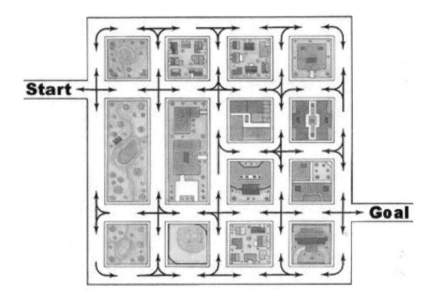

The Twisty Maze definitely requires making many, many copies, because there will be, collectively, a heap of failed attempts at navigating the maze—and obeying the left-and-right rules at every flagstone—and ending up at the GOAL. The mathematical concept that lies at correctly orienting yourself is called *parity*. At one Family Math Night in 2016, I had a seven-year-old girl spend the entire night trying to solve the maze. I told her mother that she was now hard-wired to become a mathematician!

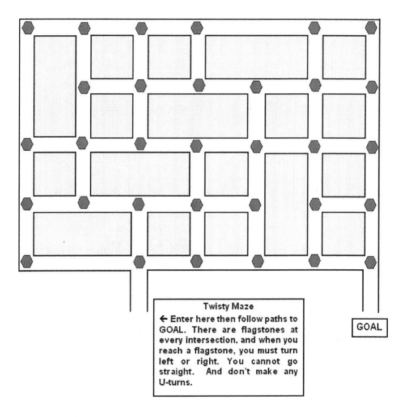

Twisty Maze

← Enter here then follow paths to GOAL. There are flagstones at every intersection, and when you reach a flagstone, you must turn left or right. You cannot go straight. And don't make any U-turns.

GOAL

mazelog.com

Roll Them Bones

Dice are quite abundant in many classrooms today, and they are often seen as nice visual tweets on Twitter to support math facts about grouping and multiplying. Here we are going to share some rather unusual configurations of dice that will help students have some fun explorations of basic probability.

Rock, Paper, Scissors

Kids know this game all too well. Many playgrounds at recess will have students go through this ritual when deciding who should go first. In 2008, Sam Kass created a five-level variant of this classic game. The game rose to prominence that year in the television show *The Big Bang Theory*, in which the character Sheldon unveiled the game in the episode "The Lizard Rock Expansion." Four years later, in the episode "The Rothman Disintegration," Sheldon would proudly exclaim, "All hail Sam Kass!"

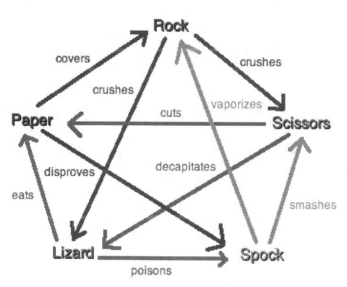

Image from Plus Maths,
plus.maths.org/content/non-transitiv-dice

It turns out there is a dice version of this game, in which, depending on what dice you pick, it will have both vulnerable and attacking qualities in comparison to another die. While there are lots of variants, we shall stick with the one that contains three dice.

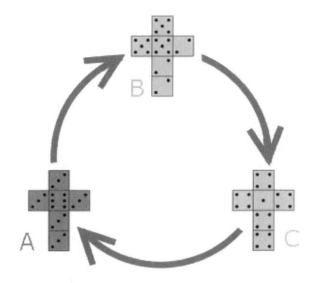

In the above example, A beats B, B beats C, and C beats A. By "beats," we mean that in the long run of head-to-head rolling and recording the highest number rolled, one die will beat another die. The best way to illustrate this with students is to make a regular 6 × 6 grid and compare the results of all thirty-six combinations when two dice are rolled. In the picture below, you can see that die A has a better chance of beating die B.

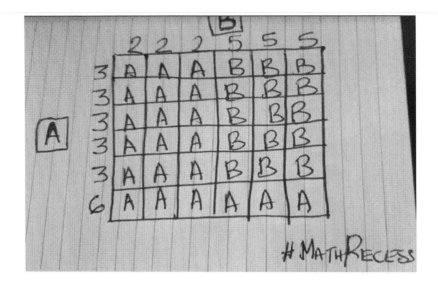

Another kind of dice that has some high-school factorization involved in the construction is called Sicherman Dice. These dice have nontraditional numbers on the faces of the dice, *however*, they have exactly the same probability distribution as regular dice. On regular dice, there are six ways to roll a 7. Similarly, on Sicherman Dice, there are also six ways—it's just they occur with some weirder pairings.

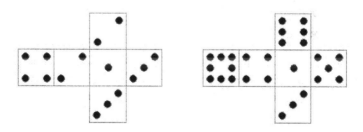

+	1	2	2	3	3	4
1	2	3	3	4	4	5
3	4	5	5	6	6	7
4	5	6	6	7	7	8
5	6	7	7	8	8	9
6	7	8	8	9	9	10
8	9	10	10	11	11	12

The possible rolls of a pair of Sicherman dice

If you would like to learn about how these dice are constructed and the "quite normal" probability distribution they create, read the excellent article, "Let 'Em Roll," in *Plus Magazine*. Incidentally, both Sicherman and Non-Transitive Dice can be bought rather cheaply on the internet.

Best Tech

There is a lot of technology out there, and as you get closer to the beginning of elementary school, the bar for a digital interface in learning mathematics must be held extremely high. In the early years, children should at least have a tactile experience with mathematics— blocks, counters, scales, shapes. Even the best technology needs to be part of a blended classroom. Books, puzzles, games, toys, and pencil and paper should not compete with technology. They should work in simpatico. There is no value in creating false dichotomies of how and when to use resources. The technology that we like honors the picture on the following page.

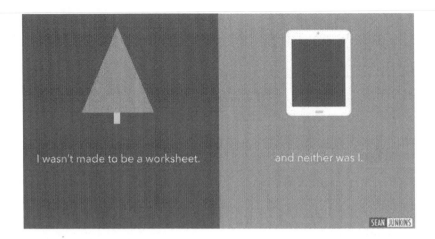

I wasn't made to be a worksheet.   and neither was I.

SEAN JUNKINS

Brainquake: brainquake.com

Led by Stanford University Professor Keith Devlin, this app is the best for building strong number sense—the foundation of all mathematical thinking.

Happy Numbers: happynumbers.com

Happy Numbers is a K–5–aligned platform that pushes children to think about mathematics in both conventional and unconventional ways. The design elements are clear, playful, and lots of fun. [SMP: 1, 6, and 7]

Zorbits: zorbits.com

Another vital resource in the K–3 years of introduction to mathematics. It reinforces the ideas that mathematics is a journey/adventure with a playful storyline, capturing the imagination of students with whimsical characters and professional narration.

Dragonbox: dragonbox.com

Dragonbox is the best app for developing algebraic skills. The apps are available for children ages five to twelve. The creative representations and high level of interactive play promotes strong algebraic reasoning in an authentically fun way.

Buzzmath: buzzmath.com

Buzzmath is the only math platform that incorporates rich mathematical history. To access this part of the platform, students have to demonstrate mastery of curriculum topics by earning gold stars. Buzzmath has an award-winning badge system that promotes self-directed learning and intrinsic motivation. [all SMPs except 4]

Square Root Marbles: squarerootmarbles.com

A great little app from the people at One on Epsilon, a company out of Australia. The game involves guiding a marble through increasingly complex mazes and going through operations including the "gate-keeper," square root. Builds strong number sense in a creative and clever way.

Brilliant: brilliant.org

One of the best places for getting a rich variety of math problems, puzzles, and ideas. Brilliant truly represents the heart of everything that encapsulates deep mathematical thinking.

MathArtFun: mathartfun.com

This is a great website that not only links math and art together, it also sells many of the activities that are described on this site.

Catching Grasshoppers

In the span of a week in 2018, I game across two math puzzles that I had never seen before, and they both had to do with grasshoppers! The first one can be found in an Ivan Moscovich book called *The Puzzle Universe: A History of Mathematics in 315 Puzzles*. As you can see, the lengths of the line segment increase by one. The grasshopper's goal is to start at the left endpoint and land on the right endpoint. The grasshopper, while being able to jump forward or backward, must increase her jump by one unit each time. Landing back at the starting point (unit length 3) is not a solution. The first nontrivial solution is with a length of four units—1F, 2F, 3B, 4F (F is for Forward and B is for Backward).

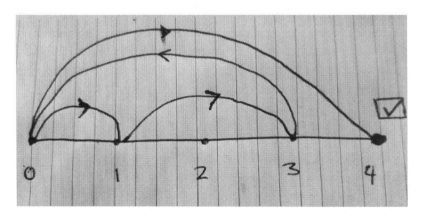

There is actually some deep mathematics behind which segment lengths provide solutions. In the first forty lengths, there are sixteen solutions! Have a go at them with your class and see how many they can find.

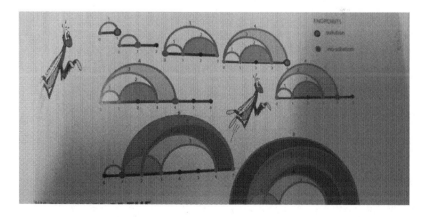

The second grasshopper puzzle is also based on jumping, but with different rules. Imagine five grasshoppers, each sitting on the tread of a tire.

Grasshoppers can jump right or left. The sizes of their jumps are based on how many grasshoppers are on a particular tread—grasshopper power! In the above picture, every grasshopper can only have a jump length of one. The other key rule is that the grasshoppers must always jump on top of one another. They can never land on an empty tread. The goal is to have all the grasshoppers on top of each other. The full solution, extension ideas, and a downloadable PDF file can be found in the link below.

Grasshopper Jump Fest
bit.do/mathrecess7

Desert Island Book List

Having books filled with rich mathematical content, colorful history, and compelling problems and discussions creates not only a nice repository of resources, but also an insatiable appetite for learning more mathematics. There are thousands of books on mathematics. In this collection are books focused on the ideas just discussed, and we know that that you, the teacher, will know when and how to implement them!

- Benjamin, Arthur. *The Joy of Mathematics*. Chantilly, VA: Teaching Co., 2007.
- Brown, Jason I. *Our Days Are Numbered: How Mathematics Orders Our Lives*. Toronto: Emblem Editions, 2010.
- Burger, Edward B., and Michael Starbird. *Coincidences, Chaos, and All That Math Jazz: Making Light of Weighty Ideas*. New York: W.W. Norton, 2006.
- Charemza, Wojciech. *Guesstimation*. Leicester, UK: Dept. of Economics, University of Leicester, 1998.
- Diack, Hunter. *Thinking in Numbers*. Nottingham, UK: Ray Palmer, 1963.
- Droujkova, Maria, James Tanton, and Yelena McManaman. *Avoid Hard Work!: ...and Other Encouraging Mathematical Problem-Solving Tips for the Young, the Very Young, and the Young at Heart*. Cary, NC: Delta Stream Media, 2016.
- Eastaway, Rob. *How Many Socks Make a Pair?* London: Aurum Press Ltd, 2014.
- Fradkin, A. O., A. B. Bishop, and Mark Gonyea. *Funville Adventures*. Cary, NC: Delta Stream Media, 2017.
- Gardner, Martin. *Mathematics Magic and Mystery*. Minooka, IL: bnpublishing.com, 2012.

- Lockhart, Paul. *A Mathematician's Lament*. New York: Bellevue Literary Press, 2009.
- Lockhart, Paul. *Arithmetic*. Cambridge, MA: Belknap Harvard, 2019.
- Moscovich, Ivan, and Hal Robinson. *The Puzzle Universe: A History of Mathematics in 315 Puzzles*. Richmond Hill, ON, Canada: Firefly Books, 2015.
- Orlin, Ben. *Math with Bad Drawings: Ideas + Stick Figures = Enlightenment*. New York: Hachette Books, 2018.
- Orlin, Ben. *Math with Bad Drawings: Illuminating the Ideas That Shape Our Reality*. New York: Hachette Books, 2018.
- Pappas, Theoni. *The Magic of Mathematics: Discovering the Spell of Mathematics*. San Carlos, CA: Wide World Pub./ Tetra, 2002.
- Parker, Matt. *Things to Make and Do in the Fourth Dimension*. London: Penguin Books, 2015.
- Paulos, John Allen. *A Mathematician Reads the Newspaper*. New York: Basic Books, 2013.
- Rosenthal, Jeffrey S. *Struck by Lightning*. London: Granta, 2008.
- Santos, Aaron. *How Many Licks?: or, How to Estimate Damn Near Anything*. Philadelphia: Running Press, 2009.
- Singh, Simon. *The Simpsons and Their Mathematical Secrets*. New York: Bloomsbury USA, 2013.
- Southall, Ed, and Vincent Pantaloni. *Geometry Snacks*. St Albans, UK: Tarquin Publ., 2017.
- Stewart, Ian. *Flatterland: Like Flatland Only More So*. London: Pan, 2003.
- Stewart, Ian. *How to Cut a Cake: and Other Mathematical Conundrums*. Oxford, UK: Oxford University Press, 2006.

- Stewart, Ian. *Professor Stewart's Cabinet of Mathematical Curiosities.* London: Profile, 2010
- Tanton, James. *Thinking Mathematics: Volumes 1 and 2.* N.p. Lulu Press, 2011
- Weinstein, Lawrence, and John A. Adam. *Gue??Timation 2.0: Solving the World's Problems on the Back of a Napkin.* Princeton, NJ: Princeton University Press, 2012.

Tangrams and Beyond

Teachers, elementary teachers especially, appreciate the tactile interaction that playing with shapes incorporates. Tangrams are the most familiar shape puzzles that are incorporated in the classroom. The tangram puzzles involve making a familiar shape out of other familiar shapes such as squares, triangles, rhombuses, and trapezoids. Some of these puzzles can be rather tough. Some of the toughest, in fact, use very few pieces to construct some very familiar shapes.

The ones below have their own station at my Family Math Nights. One of my favorite pictures taken at these festive celebrations of mathematics is the one below—the *funstration* was at full throttle.

As Dan Meyer said in his groundbreaking TED Talk in 2010, "students need patience for irresolution." For these puzzles, you will need lots of patience! The psychological state of students in these patches of irresolution is critical in determining how well they will fare when faced with more complex problems. We should aim to modify this to *passion for irresolution*!

I would recommend photocopying the pictures, and perhaps enlarging them. Paper works, but for my Family Math Nights, I use sturdier Bristol board. You can actually purchase wooden versions of these on the internet, which, of course, will lead you to the answers!

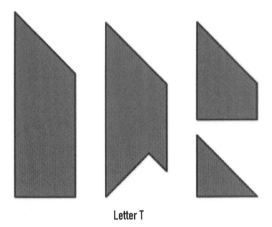

Letter T

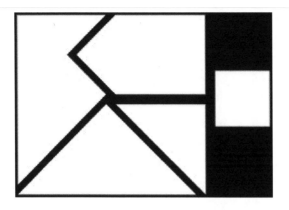

Square

Plus Sign

Best Websites

There are lots of really good math websites, but there are a select few that we find ourselves going to over and over again. We think you will be able to pull out some amazing puzzles, questions, and ideas from the sites listed here. Interestingly, five are from the United Kingdom.

Math for Love (mathforlove.com)
Plus Maths (plus.maths.org)
NRICH (nrich.org)
Julia Robinson Math Festival (jrmf.org)
Wild Maths (wild.maths.org)
Maths Ed Resource (mathsedideas.blogspot.com)
Math Pickle (mathpickle.com)

Twitter Peeps

One of the best ways to stay connected and keep your learning fluid and relevant is to connect with people on social media. Many of you are already on Twitter and engaging in dialogue that pushes not only your classroom teaching but the math community as a whole toward disruptive play! In terms of the K–8 domain of math content and pedagogy and innovative classroom ideas, you would do no better than Margie Pearse's amazing pinned list on her Twitter page (@pearce_margie)—more than two hundred passionate math education folks!

Golomb Rulers

There are many singular ideas in mathematics that quickly capture the spirit and imagination for pursuing mathematics. You know that self-directed and self-motivating longing for mathematics. I mean, how else would you desire all your students to view mathematics through this longer lens? Intrinsically of course!

Golomb rulers, named after Solomon Golomb, who studied prime numbers at the doctorate level at Harvard University, is one such idea. This exercise takes something that every kid has seen and used in public schools, the ruler, and turns it into a fantastic voyage into combinatorial number theory at the university level!

Let's scale things down for the little kiddies. Do you remember when you wanted to measure two inches? Did you always measure from 0 to the 2? After a while, didn't you just randomly select any two numbers that provided a gap of two inches? I know I did.

It is this kind of play that is the foundation of these Golomb rulers. Here is the classic Golomb ruler of order five and length eleven. What this means is that you can put five markings on a ruler without repeating a measurement less than a length of 11.

For example, if you wanted to measure a distance of five, you would use the marking of four and nine—and there is no other way to measure this. However, there is one length missing from one to eleven in this ruler. Can you find it? Can your students find it? Wouldn't it be fun to create this ruler in class?

There are different Golomb rulers. In 1984, mathematicians came up with a ruler that was order twenty-five, and its length was 480. Even today a shorter ruler having twenty-five markings and no length repeated has not been found.

Inspirational Math Quotes

Go deep enough in anything and
you will find mathematics.
—Dean Schlicler

The art of proposing a question must be
held of higher value than solving it.
—Georg Cantor

The only way to learn mathematics is to do mathematics.
—Paul Halmos

There should be no such thing as boring mathematics.
—Edsger Dijkstra

Sometimes the questions are complicated,
and the answers are simple.
—Dr. Seuss

If you stop at general math, then you will
only make general money.
—Snoop Dogg

Mathematics is one of the great emanations of the human
spirit, to be valued in of itself like art or poetry.
—Oswald Veblen

Mathematics expresses values that reflect the cosmos, including
orderliness, balance, harmony, logic, and abstract beauty.
—Deepak Chopra

Mathematics is the cheapest science. Unlike physics or chemistry, it does not require any expensive equipment. All one needs for mathematics is a pencil and paper.
—Polya George

Mathematics is the art of explanation.
—Paul Lockhart

I abandoned the assigned problems in standard calculus textbooks and followed my curiosity. Wherever I happened to be—a Vegas casino, Disneyland, surfing in Hawaii, or sweating on the elliptical in Boesel Green Microgym—I asked myself, "Where is the calculus in this experience?"
—Jennifer Ouellette

Mathematics knows no races or geographical boundaries; for mathematics, the cultural world is one country.
—David Hilbert

Good, he did not have enough imagination to become a mathematician.
—David Hilbert (Upon hearing that, one of his students had dropped out to study poetry.)

I know numbers are beautiful. If they aren't beautiful, nothing is.
—Paul Erdős

The main point is not quantity or speed— the main point is quality of thought.
—Jane Gilman

The language of mathematics, scientific observations, and our perceptivity together knit the window to reality.
—Neeti Sinha

We tend to teach mathematics as a long list of rules. You learn them in order and you have to obey them, because if you don't obey them you get a C-. This is not mathematics. Mathematics is the study if things that come out a certain way because there is no other way they could possibly be.
—Jordan Ellenberg

If the institution of mathematics told a story ...
how would it end?
—Lindsey Drage

Math is a very peculiar thing, for in it all numbers
have a double but not all have halves.
—Willa Valentine

That's because, if correct, a mathematical formula expresses an eternal truth about the universe. Hence no one can claim ownership of it; it is ours to share. Rich or poor, black or white, young or old—no one can take these formulas away from us. Nothing in this world is so profound and elegant, and yet so available to all.
—Edward Frenkel

I guess a sock is also a geometric shape—technically—
but I don't know what you'd call it. A socktagon?
—Stephen King

Math Snacks

The questions and puzzles here are an assortment of bite-size problems, perfect to nibble on, sometimes shining light on an idea in fun way—like exponents (wink!). Problems like these tend to be quite inclusive because there isn't a ton of language to declutter or information to unpack. It's like traveling *mathematically light* with your classroom, which at times is more than appropriate.

- Two children weigh 160 pounds together. The oldest weighs 120 pounds more. How much do they each weigh?
- If you toss a die six times, what is the probability that every number is different?
- What number is the same when added to 5 as when multiplied by 5?
- What is the square root of 100 percent?
- Move only one digit to make the following equation correct: $101-102 = 1$
- Rearrange the digits in $76 = 24$ to make the statement true.
- Aidan owns a plot of land that is sixty yards long and thirty yards wide. There is a fence post at every corner and along every side spaced three yards apart. How many total fence posts are there?
- Raya made thirty-four points in a basketball game with twelve shots. If she scored all her points just shooting two- or three-point shots, how many of each did she score?
- Without using a calculator, how can you tell that the number 576,380,842 is not a perfect square?
- If $x + y = 5$ and $xy = 12$, what does $x-1 + y-1$ equal? Hint: It's much easier than it looks!
- If $x + y = 7$ and $x^2 + y^2 = 50$, what does xy equal?

- The Postage Stamp Problem: Years ago I bought a very large supply of stamps in two denominations—eighteen cents and thirteen cents. I know that I cannot put exact postage on a letter that would cost me fourteen cents. Are there any others that I cannot make postage for? (This is a trick problem because the truth is that there are many, not a huge number, of values I cannot make up; but there is a number somewhere in the future beyond which I can make ANY value. Can you find it and prove that it must be so?)

New York Times Numberplay

Although this blog is, sadly, no longer around, all of the puzzles and articles are still available. I had the wonderful opportunity to write several articles a few years back. It was Dan Finkel who suggested to the editor of the Numberplay, Gary Antonick (who ended up writing a back-cover review of my first book), that I should be a regular contributor. There are so many number puzzles that came from here that I absolutely love, but I think the "Tax Collector" is my favorite. It can get even the youngest kids thinking about numbers and building strategies with basic math facts. The problem comes courtesy of Dan Finkel. The link to the entire article is wordplay.blogs.nytimes.com/2015/04/13/finkel-4/

Tax Collector

Tax Collector is played like this: Start with a collection of paychecks, from one dollar to twelve dollars. You can choose any paycheck to keep. Once you choose, the tax collector gets all paychecks remaining that are factors of the number you chose. The tax collector must receive payment after every move. If you have no moves that give the tax collector a paycheck, then the game is over, and the tax collector gets all the remaining paychecks.

The goal is to beat the Tax Collector! Can you do it? [SMPs: 1, 2, 7]

Cows in the Classroom

Sometimes in life, you just get lucky. I got to start my high school teaching career with Pete Harrison, one of the best math teachers I have ever met. For four years, I got to teach with Peter. Although he produced many astounding resources and problem sets, he is perhaps most famous for creating his "Cows In the Classroom" (bovinemath. com). The Cow questions generally revolve around fields (which represent a whole number of cows) and bridges (which represent some operational relationship between adjacent fields). It might sound simple, but with this rather goofy template, Peter takes students from basic addition and subtraction ideas to number theory and algebra and even to the topic of eigenvectors!

One of my favorite questions from the Cows collection turned into a whole blog.

Sunil Singh
Sep 5 · 5 min read

The Greatest K to 12 Math Problem Ever

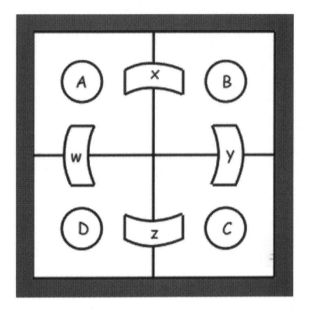

[SMPs: 1, 2, 3, 4, 7, 8]

What I find absolutely fascinating about this question is that not only can it be solved by anyone in K–12, it can be solved within the mathematical understanding and maturity possessed at various grade levels. The problem has you put single digits into each of the eight unknowns without repetition—imagine elementary kids playing with so many cloaked numbers—such that the bridges represent the sum of adjacent fields. So if A equals 1, and B equals 2, then x equals 3.

Elementary kids can simply guess and check their answers. It's not easy, but they will completely understand the problem! Maybe they can even be asked whether there are certain numbers that can't be bridge numbers (one and two!).

Middle-school students can still use guess and check, but maybe they can be asked to just label the bridges and fields with Es (even) and Os (odd). Maybe the structure here in terms of just even and odd numbers might give some insight.

Finally, in high school, students can test their algebraic sophistication to produce a generalized result. Full solutions are available on the website, but if you would like to contact Peter Harrison directly, and ask for more Cows stuff, he will be more than happy to send you everything he can still find! (peterjharrison@rogers.com)

The Rabbit Hole

It deserves a chapter all its own. See you there!

QUESTIONS FOR DEEPER DISCUSSION

1. Choose one of the two-player games above and play it ten times against a single opponent. Force yourself to lose each time. Talk to that person about what you did, why you did it, and what it taught you about the game.

2. Create a game station in your classroom where students can go when they need a break. Curate a few of these games into that station, adding and subtracting some every few weeks. Take note of this station's effect on your students.

3. Commit to playing as many of these games as is humanly possible at your next family holiday gathering. Listen for laughter, sounds of frustration, and shouts of victory. Then pat yourself on the back for bringing so much joy into the world, instead of listening to your crotchety uncle decry the downfall of humanity because of "kids these days."

CHAPTER 5

Finn-n-Fun

Schooling is about finding your happiness...
—Unnamed Finnish teacher

In Chapter 3, I brought up the idea of Finnish schools, I'd like to discuss them in a little more detail here. First, I recommend you take a few minutes and watch the video that the code below links to; it is by documentarian Michael Moore. I am not always a fan of his work, but in this instance he highlights some important differences between Finnish schools and those in systems like the United States. In this video, a Finnish teacher describes the goal of schooling as, "about finding your happiness..." Elsewhere teachers are asked about their homework policies, to which they reply, "We don't give any homework..." Moore is stunned and asks incredulously, "So a child could leave school, go home, and climb trees all day?" The teacher replies something akin to, "Oh yes, and while they are up in that tree maybe they will find some very interesting insect or leaf that they will bring back to school to talk about..."

A Documentary on Finland's Schools
bit.do/mathrecess-moorevideo

It might seem strange to devote an entire chapter to Finland and its education system, but bear with me a moment. If you have seen Moore's semiviral video, you'll understand. Finland went from having schools performing at about the same level as the United States on the Organization for Economic Cooperation and Development's triennial survey, the Programme for International Student Assessment, to being among the top three all the time. Its rise didn't happen over the course of a century but inside of three decades of concerted effort.

I am a late-in-life academic. By that I mean I earned my doctoral degree (making me an official academic) in my fifties. At age fifty, I was working as a university math professor with a master's degree, teaching undergraduate students who wanted to become teachers, and some of the deeper ideas in mathematics had fascinated me. Via a bizarre and complex set of coincidences, I found myself in a doctoral program in a research university some 264 miles from my home. The exact number of miles is embedded in my brain because I drove the distance literally hundreds of times in three and a half years. I spent a good deal of time in graduate school working in comparative studies of international education systems, and I had been impressed with what was happening on the ground in Finland. By the time I was ready to graduate, I was back permanently in my hometown, conducting research while working as a professor of education. Shortly after I completed my final dissertation defense, I had the opportunity to travel to Finland with some other members of the faculty at my university, and I jumped at the chance.

My wife, Rose, also encouraged me to go. We put together the funds, and literally hours after receiving my doctoral hood from my favorite advisor and professor, my wife was booting me out of the car door at the Bradley Terminal at LAX. Talk about wild and crazy times!

To prepare for the trip, I had read Pasi Salsberg's *Finnish Lessons 2.0*, met with colleagues, and, in keeping with the academic in me, boned up on heaps of research. It was a whirlwind trip of less than ten days, touring several universities, learning centers, teacher education programs, and schools. We also visited the Ministry of Education's statistical analysis experts. Those of us on the journey were excited to see this system firsthand and hear about it from as many perspectives as possible.

When I watch Moore's video, I'm fine until about the three-and-a-half-minute mark. That's when, during a faculty meeting, a young female teacher in the back says, "School is about finding your happiness..." I always have to stop and cry for a while after she says this. My heart breaks to think of how few American children experience any happiness in schooling beyond their earliest years. The education model portrayed in Moore's video is one that focuses on an entirely different set of goals for learning. Nothing within that culture is about using standardized tests to measure growth against some norm-referenced collection of arbitrary standards.

In the past two years, I have visited Finland twice for the express purpose of coming to understand what it is that the Finns are doing, Michael Moore's editorializing aside. I was incredulous when it came to the claim that Finnish kids have no homework; they do get some, albeit a remarkably small amount relative to the average US student. Students might have a few short- or high-interest tasks to accomplish away from school, but the practice of assigning forty-some problems from a page in a textbook is no longer alive and well in Finnish schools. But you can call me a believer in the idea that the Finns place diminished importance on grading their children against each other. Formative assessment is replacing heaps of summative assessments. Within the past three years, the Finnish national curriculum has been rewritten to include a multidisciplinary requirement in each year of schooling. This will require a completely different method of assessment, and there is no way to assign a single letter or numeric grade to such a task. This is no small idea; if a teacher gives an assignment that requires a student to incorporate and integrate such diverse fields of study as math and art, or biology and history, with the goal being the student learns and performs well in all the subjects...applying a single grade could be called malpractice.

What was abundantly clear during my time in Finland is that teachers there have greater autonomy. They have more freedom to choose, based on their professional judgment, what, when, and how their students will learn in their classrooms. They have shorter school days, and they assign a far smaller number of mindless practice problems in mathematics and other subjects. Teachers are more concerned about how their students' days are going than how they are doing on homework.

Several vivid scenes come to mind when I reflect on my visits to Finland. The first took place on my first trip in 2016. The group I was with was visiting a city called Jyvaskyla in central Finland. In this city is one of the few universities that trains teachers. I was invited to visit the classroom of Dr. Kristof Fenyvesi, a Hungarian-born immigrant to Finland. This class was listening to reports from student teachers who had been out the past few weeks trying out their teaching skills. There were roughly sixteen students, three visitors including myself, and three professors—one math, one physics, and one arts integration. The students, all in their early- to mid-twenties, had been assigned the task of creating an integrated set of arts and mathematics lessons. They were reporting on how the lessons had gone in class.

What was mind-boggling was that this was in no way a yikes-we-are-trying-something-subversive-and-out-of-the-box moment. All of the students and faculty were matter-of-fact about the concept of integrating the topics. The educators offered many pointers—"Did you think to include something about so-called Special Right Triangles here?" or "Why did you select these art materials?" The student teachers were clearly not experts, but they were not trying something that seemed so foreign to them that they could not conceive of it. This process lies in stark contrast to my experiences as a student teacher, teacher, and teacher educator in the United States. I came to the idea of integrating math, science, and arts slowly and almost rebelliously over time. Today in the United States, it is still considered a radical approach.

On my second trip to Finland in 2017, I visited a small elementary school in that same city of Jyvaskyla. The children enter the school and remove their shoes right away. This is good for at least two reasons—one, it reduces the custodial needs of the facility (Finland winters are pretty snowy), and two, many children prefer to be shoeless, and this sets up a comfort level in the learning environment, almost a recess-like atmosphere throughout their classroom experiences. The children are their own custodians, cooks, and monitors throughout the building. Like most schools, art projects, and science projects dot the halls, and the sounds of children's voices are everywhere. At lunch the kids take turns serving each other the meals that they also take part in preparing. Shoes, coats, boots, backpacks, and all manner of personal gear are stowed—semineatly because they are kids, after all—in an area near the front of the building without fear or even a second thought that these items might not be there when they return for them.

At this school, I visited the classroom of Jukka Sinnemaki, who was a 2018 finalist for Global Teacher of the Year, and it was easy to see why. His room was innovative, even by Finnish standards. He employed a philosophy of learning predicated on the body being an extension of the brain—embodied learning, as it is called in research. Around the room are chin-up bars, treadmills, data collection tools for fitness, and large elastic bands for assisting children who might not be able to lift themselves up to do a pull-up at first. You might be thinking he doubles as the physical education teacher, but you'd be wrong. He is the sixth- and seventh-grade math teacher. His students can get exercise anytime they want. They can do all their daily learning while walking on a treadmill, contribute to classroom discussions while pushing themselves to a new personal record on the pull-up bars, or any of a number of other physical challenges.

This level of autonomy is built into the schooling system throughout Finland. Teachers have great latitude to teach in a way that resonates with their own personal philosophy, their own sense of gravitas about learning. Students are considered to be young, autonomous, capable humans rather than small, not yet fully human creatures. These contrasts are stark in my mind. Children with self-efficacy versus children who can't do because they are seldom asked to do. The Finns might complain about the next generation being lazy or having too much hair or too many tattoos, just like other countries, but they value their differences. They also know that they have raised reliable, fun-loving, recess-ready adults who can reason and solve problems. International educational attainment measures agree with them.

What more is there to say? Is it possible to incorporate a sense that education is about helping other humans pursue and find their happiness along with some form of utilitarianism that we in the United States seem to value so highly? Could other nations also incorporate this sense of play and active learning into their daily practices? Would it be possible to get schools past a warehousing of children while their parents work all day and into places that empower and create effective and happy humans?

This book is mostly about mathematics, and this chapter is mostly not. Why did we include it? Sunil and I are advocates for more than just a different perspective of mathematics. We both see problems with the education system in our respective countries. We consistently encourage more playful and engaging approaches to every subject.

When Sunil is having children build a fourth-order Sierpinski Sponge out of Legos, as he did when he exhibited at the 2017 Bridges Math and Art Conference in Waterloo, Ontario, Canada, he isn't merely trying to teach about the number 45. He is looking to increase joy, to help children, and quite a large number of adults, find a measure of happiness with their accomplishment. Along the way, they are collaborating, arguing, experimenting, talking about and around ideas, and engaging in life for the singular cause of doing.

That a nation, yes, a whole nation, has adopted this attitude about schooling is why we devoted an entire chapter to Finland. We wanted to say, "It is possible, this dream of ours!"

"... you may say that I am a dreamer,
but I'm not the only one ..."

One last Finnish vignette. In my 2017 visit, I was invited to provide an in-service training to some teachers. I presented with two other professors, my friend and colleague Kristof Fenyvesi and Dr. Osmo Pekkonen. I planned out my workshop and figured I would include some paper folding work on hexa-flexagons and demonstrate the trick that Sunil outlines in Chapter 2 of this book. (Yes, we even overlap on the tricks we pull on kids. It's terrible.) What I understood was that I would present to two groups of teachers in two separate workshops, but my Hungarian-Finnish is near zero, and Kristof, who had invited me, is almost too much like me in that we believe details are what happens in the moment and are not necessarily planned for. At any rate, I did not know that children would be in attendance. But there they were! The teachers brought in students as active learning guinea pigs to demonstrate the importance and strength of the techniques we were employing.

This was such a difference from the in-service environments I was accustomed to in the states. All of the teachers were engaged, the children were engaged, and laughter and learning took place in both groups. Mistakes were welcomed, cherished even. No teachers were checked out in the back of the room grading papers with pouty faces. The children interacted with the teachers as co-problem solvers. When the workshop was finished, Osmo began a mini history lesson regarding the mathematics he had delivered. He included some of the work of Carl Friedrich Gauss, a nineteenth-century mathematician (you will meet him in an upcoming chapter), and Benoit Mandelbrot, a twentieth-century mathematician. Soon he was discussing fractals, geometry, history, art, problem solving, poetry, and fiction. The students were following along, and then he ventured to ask me, without any warning, for any thoughts on the subject. Soon we were in that state of *flow* that Sunil mentioned in Chapter 2. Two professors from disparate backgrounds, who had never met prior to a half hour before the workshops began, were finishing each other's jokes and stories.

I tell this story not merely because it illustrates how Osmo and I developed a friendship and professional relationship based on our mutual interests, which is an illustration of why Sunil and I chose to write Chapter 10 of this book; I tell it because this sort of thing could not have happened in a less play-oriented culture or with a group of people who would never seek to learn alongside the children they are teaching. The recess Sunil and I are advocating is for the adults in the

The group of Finnish teachers, students, and me, having constructed a small geodesic dome together, gather under it for a group photo. That's me on the far left. We are in the City Hall of the City of Kuopio in eastern Finland.

room as much as for the children. Learn alongside them, with them, while you teach them; everyone will be happier because you do.

Epilogue: Lately Sunil and I have been making a social media push to have people within the education world accept the possibility of having a "blank slate" moment, one in which a society would give itself permission to re-examine what it means to educate the citizenry of a nation. Horace Mann, who some consider to be the primary crafter of the United States' original public-school system, had it easy: There were no entrenched systems, no tired traditions of what schools should look like. He was able to cast a vision without having to constantly be pressed with, "But we don't do it that way!" or, "These kids all need to know their times-tables before they can learn other math!" stereotypes. We are advocating that we, by this we mean the overwhelming majority of educationally mediocre-performing school systems, need to give ourselves a "blank slate" and think hard about what it means to be an educated member of the society in which people live, breathe, and have their being. Finland did this, and this is why this chapter is in this book.

The nation as a whole had a discussion among those who were concerned, sought out common ground to speak from, set common goals, and established high standards that include joy, love of learning, technical prowess, connected thinking, and rich support for those in need of it. If it can be done, why not here? If it should be done, why not now?

QUESTIONS FOR DEEPER DISCUSSION

1. It has been said that Finland was able to make this happen because it became a part of the culture and the nation's commitment to excellence. What can you do in your classroom to foster a culture of excellence while maintaining individualism as valued?

2. What changes in perspective toward mathematics, and more broadly, education can you adopt that would impact your teaching and classroom environment?

3. The Finnish commitment to learning through play is real. How can you adopt a more playful methodology to your classroom?

CHAPTER 6

Storytelling

Stories have to be told or they die, and when they die, we can't remember who we are or why we are here.

—Sue Monk Kidd

Nobody is immune from the magic and power of storytelling. It's an art form through which people of all ages are able to connect thoughts and ideas to meaningful emotions. Storytelling can teach us about intimacy, beauty, and the truth of our shared humanity. When we are young, stories and *storytelling* often hold us in a tight grip. They're a language that comes quite naturally, one that we know and love and easily use to explain the world around us. As we age, however, many of us become less proficient in the language of stories and storytelling. Thanks to myriad factors—technology, social media, demanding careers—adults grow increasingly removed from the emotional connections found in storytelling.

We certainly have more information at our fingertips, but it often seems that humans are acting more like computers—focused on housing massive amounts of content and mastering the required procedures. Empathy, a critical element of storytelling, often tacitly gives way to efficiency. Productivity and proficiency thrive. Passion, if it was ever there, withers away.

The teaching of mathematics becomes entangled in all of this. Its vibrancy and color are found in countless stories over thousands of years, but often get shaded into obscurity. A distillate of facts, equations, and *procedures* remains, most having anonymous origins. Origins are critical life threads that lead back to human inspiration. They are part of the fabric of connecting, often to a human you will never know. Mathematics is a most human endeavor spanning the spectrum of emotions—from struggle and sorrow to discovery and delight. It's the greatest story *rarely* told.

The story of mathematics is even more powerful when we realize it is inextricably linked to the story of our students and ourselves. In the picture below, we have used the Borromean rings to illustrate this beautiful trinity.

If you notice, the removal of any one ring means the other two will fall apart. Listen to your students, wear your heart on your sleeve, and dive deep into the history of mathematics. It is where we find our souls. In January 2017, Junaid Mubeen, who holds a doctorate in mathematics from Oxford University, wrote a beautiful article commenting on the emptiness of math without history.

Mathematics without history is soulless
π through the ages

The quote below from the article is most representative of the aspirations of this book.

> It should be no different for aspiring mathematicians. Students need to understand that mathematical ideas do not just spring into being. They develop gradually as humans explore and ask questions, often with immense struggle, reward, and surprise (is it really obvious that π is constant?). The process of mathematical discovery is messy and uncertain, even if the end result appears clean.

It is in these stories that we will find so much of what we need to teach and connect. Isn't that why we are here? Connection. It's the heart of the matter. We have pondered that question so carefully that the answer that we will share is the chapter that closes this book. For now we are going to share stories that will serve to inspire and underscore the importance of spending time with ideas and problems and letting casual anecdotes and reflections flow naturally. We want to show that students value mathematics not only through traditional experiences of solving problems and giving answers but also through more qualitative moments that are cherished enough to become stories.

The Story of Students

Several years back, I (Sunil) gathered testimonials from dozens of students from the roughly two thousand I had taught in my career. It was information that I was adding to a business loan to create The Right Angle, a math store and school. Unfortunately, two weeks before the grand opening, there was a catastrophic fire, and everything was destroyed. The whole ordeal became a midwife to a rebirth of gratitude and a re-examination of my purpose within mathematics. It is in those overwhelming testimonials, many more than a decade old, that I recalibrated my vision for mathematics.

One of the testimonials was a searing reminder of how we, as teachers, are gifted our students. That the connections we make, the risks we take, and the love we show everyday rarely goes unnoticed. It is that one that I need to share for the purposes of this book, which is about finding the courage and conviction to drastically change the way math is taught in elementary and middle schools. This student was Maddie Maher, a 15-year-old girl at the time. She was enrolled in a rigorous International Baccalaureate program in Switzerland. I taught there for one year. Why only one? My wife and I moved to Switzerland after seven years of trying to have a child. We were unsuccessful. We thought we should move from Canada and just travel at this point. Guess what? She got pregnant, and we went home. That one year in Switzerland, though, teaching kids from all around the world, would forever change how I saw mathematics education—and what I needed to do in the future.

I met Mr. Singh when I was 15, already an enthusiastic math student. He taught me in Lausanne, Switzerland, for one regrettably brief year.

He was, as he has said himself, our teacher, friend, confidant, and warrior. And he remains in this role to this day, even many years after high school ended. It is because of the impression Mr. Singh made on me that I quit my job very recently in order to pursue a career path similar to his, and to further the perception of math as a wonderful thing, beautiful and enriching. All teachers would do well to take a couple leaves from Sunil's book—though few are as fearless and dedicated as he is, anyone who hasn't opened their mind to his ideas would do well to give them a try and see how much happier everyone is as a result.

Sunil approaches teaching in a way that some greatly admired, some worried about, and some outright resented. Though when I speak of the latter two reactions, they are of his peers: His students unanimously loved his classes. We would get properly excited about learning math, and we wished that his class would go on for much longer than the slot it was allowed. His classroom became an oasis for us, a place where we knew we were understood and looked after.

The object was not to learn the bullet points in the curriculum, but to explore, and learn to do any of them using our readiness to jump into a problem and the mathematical intuition we would acquire over several months. He believed in us and encouraged us. He saw us not as kids with x topics to go before we were exam-ready, but as minds capable of doing great things.

Teenagers are delicate creatures. We would swing from feeling capable and full of energy, to totally insecure, dangerously self-deprecating, and very afraid of the future. In his classroom we were all equal, we became good friends, we helped each other to understand and to think of things in new ways. His guidance created an atmosphere of congeniality and respect. There were no chains in his class. We could listen to music, if we thought it helped us. We could work in groups or alone. If we wanted to go to the bathroom, we didn't ask, we just went. And we hurried back, for fear of missing something good.

We needed so much to know that someone cared about us as people, and that someone had our back, should something go wrong. We knew we had that in Mr. Singh. He wasn't afraid to talk openly about the things that concerned us, and to share with us his personal experiences.

Sunil was interested in us, in the stories we had to tell, and in our well-being, as well as in our education. We talked a lot about things bigger than school, of relationships and understanding your own needs, choosing a career, staying happy. And of music, chemistry, pharmacology, games.

He taught us about the curiosities of Pascal's Triangle, the weirdness of prime numbers, bad bets in poker, the secretly brilliant mathematical jokes made in *The Simpsons*, the excitingly different world of complex numbers. He taught us to search for and appreciate patterns, to look for beauty wherever we could identify or create it. Suddenly math really was everywhere. We hunted for it, discussed it in our spare time, applied these new ideas and new ways of thinking in all our other classes. We started asking questions about whether it was possible to raise a matrix to the power of matrix, or what might happen if you continued Pascal's Triangle in the wrong direction. This is the kind of thinking that advances fields, not just mathematics. You have to have the courage to think and ask things that might be considered odd or stupid, and to either have great backbone, or have someone telling you you're on the right track.

At one parent-teacher conference, Sunil told my mother and me with great conviction that I would love pure math, and that I should study it. I was flattered, but at the time couldn't imagine leaving languages behind (I studied computer science and linguistics in the end) and am only now coming to the conclusion that he was right, and that pure math is still in the cards for me. There is something fundamental and unifying about math that I would not have seen without his help.

We were not afraid to say we didn't understand something, and so we didn't play that dangerous and soul-destroying pretending game, where you act as if you know something, and as things get more and more complicated and it becomes harder and harder to extricate yourself from this lie, your sense of worth in this subject disintegrates inside you, and at some point it's too late. This is a behavior that teaching often encourages, and it is terribly unnecessary. We were unafraid to learn, even if we risked looking a bit silly now and then.

Since before Sunil's class, I loved doing math. I loved the odd modes of thinking it required, and the multiple perspectives you needed to see its patterns. But after Sunil's class, I saw it as the subject as a refuge, something constant I could return to if I felt confused or upset. (I still draw Pascal's Triangle every now and again and look for patterns in it to calm myself down.) I would explain mathematical ideas I'd gotten excited about to anyone who would listen, and this would bring me great pleasure. Math was an infinite set of things waiting to be noticed, a beautiful tapestry you could see if you concentrated really hard on just about anything.

Sunil moved back to Canada after our one year with him, for a reason we couldn't have been happier about, but we missed him greatly. The teacher who took over for our last year of school spent much of her time expressing her disapproval for the way he'd taught us, which meant we were offended, lost our drive to learn, and just plodded along as we had been used to doing in so many other classes, doing exactly what was required of us and no more. You could feel the wasted energy in that room. We had been looking forward to learning some number theory with Sunil, but our new teacher said number theory wasn't as useful as statistics, since we would all have to do some statistics at university at some point. (Not a very exciting motivator, I might add.) So we did statistics. It took a lot of time and effort, all the more so because we didn't want to understand it—it was getting in the way of something we had actually wanted to do. Sunil knew what we liked; our new teacher didn't care about that.

We all passed our exams, sure. But our spirits and enthusiasm were trodden on, and this made us very bitter, unwilling, uncreative learners, especially as we'd felt so empowered the previous year. To illustrate the contrast, I still remember most things Sunil taught me, and many of them in vivid detail. I remember next to nothing of what our second teacher imparted.

Sunil made me want to be a teacher myself, and a mathematician — to be true to these parts of myself. It is very sad news that he is judged by the fact that he does things differently (as every great person ever has), rather than how he improves the minds and lives of the young people he teaches. He made the effort to really know us, and we learned more as a result.

No other teacher I've met has succeeded in making learning quite as light and wonderful as Sunil has. His method succeeds in winning over not just your focus and mental capacities, but your heart too. He uses his students' curiosity as fuel, since it is the best kind of fuel, though it is so terribly underrated. Why else, except out of curiosity, do we ever really want to learn?

One of the biggest mistakes that is sometimes made as children start school is that we ignore their slate of raw math understanding— almost wiping it clean. We should start where they are. *What do they know about numbers? How high do you think you can count? What scares you about math? Is there anything about you that I should know that will help me make learning math fun?*

There is a beautiful quote that Francis Su often shares in his math talks across North America. Its resonating power is immeasurable:

Every being cries out to be read differently.

—Simone Weil

Mathematics must meet students where they are not only intellectually, but socially and emotionally as well. That is why social and emotional learning is such a key anchor in the burgeoning philosophy of so many schools around the world. Everything is intertwined. Mathematics is a complex subject that is heavily nuanced in how we as humans intersect and interact with it. That is why sharing stories of mathematics and celebrating its lore and legends is paramount in fostering a lifelong passion for mathematics.

Stories of Mathematics

Both Chris and I have selected a few stories—from the thousands out there—that capture the spirit of resilience and the magic of the human connection with math. They are stories that have helped inspire this book. They might seem worlds apart, but they are not. They are connected. Mathematics is a massive quilt, patched together with thousands on thousands of colorful emanations of mathematical truth. This book is a modest patch in that tapestry. All these stories are from different parts of the mathematical fabric. We want you to chase these threads and many others. We hope they will inspire you to not only weave storytelling into the teaching of mathematics but to continue to seek out stories of your own!

Bletchley Park

This nineteenth-century mansion in Buckinghamshire, England greets thousands of tourists every year. The lore of Bletchley Park was only enhanced by the 2014 film *The Imitation Game*, which focused on the code-breaking work of Alan Turing during World War II. While this is a great story, that is not why we are including it here. We are including it because of an opposite reason—the story *does not* tell the story of Bletchley Park. The machine that was employed by Hitler was not Enigma. The person who broke that code was not Alan Turing. The machine was called Lorenz. The person that broke that code and shortened the war by probably two years was William Tutte.

We will leave you a link to a trailer for a brilliant BBC documentary that tells the non-Hollywood events. This inclusion of the story of Bletchley Park is to persuade you to find the deeper truths of not just stories in math but any stories. World War II was shortened by at least two years because of a very specific and innocent communication. Intrigued? We are going to leave it to you to hunt down the gripping details.

Video link: youtube.com/watch?v=bMu8UiHJHgs

A Short History of Long Lines

In the beginning there was Euclid. This story is less about a single person than an idea. It is adapted from a talk I (Chris) have given several times, including as an Ignite Talk at the First Global Math Symposium in 2017.

Euclid, a Greek mathematician who lived in the fourth century BCE, gave us five statements to do geometry by. These statements were so obvious to him that he gave them the title of "postulate," which basically means "a thing suggested as true as the basis for reasoning, discussion, or belief," according to Google. Our modern-day definition, however, falls a bit short of what Euclid actually meant. Greeks of his era would only state as postulates things that were so obviously true as to be unquestionable. No one would dare to call into question the truthfulness of something that could be elevated to the level of a postulate, and Euclid gave us five for geometry in Book I of his *Elements*. The first four postulates are indeed quite obvious in fact. In modern language, these four are:

- It is possible to draw a straight line between any two points.
- It is possible to extend a straight line to any length.
- It is possible, given a fixed point called the center, and a length called the radius, to draw a circle.
- All right angles are equal.

The fifth postulates takes some thinking to follow:

- If a straight line that falls across two other straight lines makes two interior angles on the same side of the line that add up to less than 180 (degrees), then the two straight lines intersect on that side of the line on which those two angles are.

Yeah, I know what you are thinking—*huh*?! The first four were so simple, so elegant, so beautifully understandable. Then this thing comes along and convinces you all over again that mathematics is just some sort of word play designed to make your head hurt. In short, what this means is that the two lines in this picture that look like they will meet somewhere, will meet on the side of the crossing line where the angles inside them add up to less than 180 degrees.

Hopefully that little picture helps you understand the postulate, but it isn't critical that you do to follow our story, so let's get back to it. The fact that this "self-evident" and "standing without proof" statement was so complicated and nuanced bothered people who studied

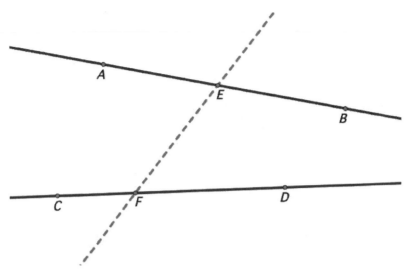

Euclid almost from the beginning. Efforts were made over the centuries to attack and to "prove" this statement.

An analogous (mathematically, it would be more accurate to say equivalent) description of the postulate is to say that if you have a line and one point not on that line, it is possible to draw one and only one line parallel to the first line. This is why it is often referred to as "The Parallel Postulate." Many people thought this postulate could be proven rather than just assumed or taken as true. For centuries some of the more famous mathematical thinkers and many less famous thinkers spent much time on this task.

One particular character, Father Giovanni Saccheri, made an interesting attempt. He started with our analogous statement about there being one and only one line through a point that is parallel to another line and decided that this statement had three possible perspectives.

1. Given that line, m, and that point, there are *no* lines through the point that are parallel.
2. Given that line, m, and that point, there is *exactly one* line through the point parallel to m.

3.   Given that line and that point there could be *many* lines parallel through the point parallel to m.

Do you see his simple genius? He sought to reduce the problem to these three separate cases, demonstrate that the first and third could never exist and therefore the second had to be the only way to the truth. Brilliant!

Unfortunately, he didn't see it all the way through. He himself was blinded by the idea that what he made up in his mind was real, just like Euclid, who was also very narrow-minded. In his treatise, *Euclid Devoid of All Flaws,* Saccheri attempted to show that options 1 and 3 were impossible, and in this he came up a little short. He fell short of his goal, but in the process, he came quite close to creating a whole new branch of geometry. That would be left for three other men in the next century to unfold.

Carl F. Gauss, Nikolai Lobachevsky, and Janos Bolyai formed an interesting collection of collaborators from across Europe in the nineteenth century, well before email or social media. Bolyai published an appendix in a textbook written by his father, Lobachevsky a short paper about two years prior, and Gauss made claims of developing these ideas on his own some ten or eleven years before either of these two. This new geometry that they discovered, which mathematicians now refer to as "hyperbolic," changes that one postulate to read like this:

Given a line L and a point not on that line P but in the same plane as that line, there are infinitely many other lines through point P that do not intersect line L.

This new geometry allows for very interesting and simultaneously counterintuitive new relationships inside the universe. One thing that gets challenged right away is the meaning of "straight" in this world. And how you measure angles. Many of the standard truths of geometry get turned on their head here. At first glance, this all sounds and seems like some mathematician's fantasy play. You might ask yourself, *Does this silliness do us any good?*

It turns out that it does. Some of the basis of Einstein's thinking on relativity is supported within a geometry like this. To cut this whole story short, Euclid gave us straight lines that allowed for parallel lines to exist in our minds. Many people attempted to attack his premise as provable and failed. Some of those efforts, however, led to the invention of a new form of geometry that turns out to have the quality of being accurate within the real cosmos we inhabit. The old rules made real the idea of parallelism (something that does not appear in our universe except in our minds); the new rules allow for different situations altogether, and these situations are more accurate depictions of what is seen in the known universe. Know the rules, break the rules, and change.

Albert's Insomnia

… and then one hundred divided by two is fifty.

It's not often that a statement like the one above results in *"oohs"* and *"aahs"* from a rowdy table in a downtown bar. But it's not often people stumble across the subtly addictive game called Albert's Insomnia. There are several ways to play this game, but the variation that allows for maximizing the mathematical and social benefit is this one.

Four cards are randomly picked from the deck. Two yellow, one blue, and one green. Yellow cards have numbers 1 to 4, blue ones 5 to 8, and green ones 9 to 12. The cards are then placed face up for everyone to see. Starting at the number 1, people take turns trying to construct "answers" from 1 and up with the cards dealt. No card can be used more than once. Not all the cards have to be used. And, as indicated, the basic operations of addition, subtraction, multiplication and division.

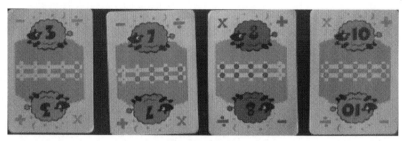

Albert's Insomnia

Here are what some of the beginning responses could look like:

1 = 8 – 7
2 = 10 ÷ (8 – 3)
3 = 3 (you can point to the card if it is available)
4 = 7 – 3
5 = 10 ÷ [8 ÷ (7 – 3)]
And so on...

Using the cards above, it was my turn to create an answer for 50. We had started at 1. In our *adult version*, we were playing with square/cube roots and factorials as well! We do this because it gives more flexibility and the possibility of creating every number—and prolonging the game.

Three beers in at the Keystone Bar in San Francisco in November 2017, I came up with: 10^sq. rt(7–3) divided by cube rt 8—which was unnecessarily hard! You could have simple done 10 × (8 – 3). Of course, that was hilariously pointed out to me by people at the table. Laughing: It's a good tonic to drink often. And Albert's Insomnia is a game that brings that out often.

I stumbled on this game a few years ago, and yes, I have suffered—thankfully—from bouts of number insomnia many, many times. The creator of the game is Rick Buchner from Savannah, Georgia. Like all wonderful things in life that have a permanence and timeless quality, Albert's Insomnia is a *simple pleasure*. I have played Albert's in various places and situations—at math conferences, at Family Math Nights, classrooms, kitchen tables, and now bars.

Albert's Insomnia. California 2017

The game, because of its structural simplicity of just cards, lends itself to an intimate huddle of participants, who are teeming with energy and excitement with the addictive gameplay. At my Family Math Nights, it is easily one of the most popular tables—parents are often standing and hovering over the cards, showcasing a *happy restlessness*. Just play, right? Play involves socialization. Socialization is the gateway to richer human connections/friendships.

One of the participants at the Keystone Bar was an art teacher. He was also attending the California STEAM 2017 Conference in San Francisco. He just came with his "math friends" to have some beers. After I made 50, it was his turn to make 51. He had been thinking about it for fifteen minutes, glued to the cards, purposefully sipping his beer. (*Note: I do not think his number is possible. Is it?*)

He also admitted to being math-phobic. Thirty minutes into the game, he was glued. Not only was he giving correct answers to his target numbers, he was trying to be creative with his responses. The power of the game is amplified when paired with elements that bring out positive association—snacks, drinks, and laughter.

Albert's Insomnia. Keystone Bar, San Francisco

I (Sunil) have seen my own son spit out chunks of ice cream with excitement in getting an elusive target number. In fact, on a road trip to Universal Studios in Hollywood, California, we were all stumped by 79. The numbers on the cards were 3, 4, 6, and 11. The five-hour car trip from San Francisco flew by as all of us were trying to crack this mathematical nut. And then, twenty minutes outside of Los Angeles, my nephew said, "I GOT IT!"

The answer is... no, you try it. You need the gift of insomnia. [SMP: 2, 6, 7, 8]

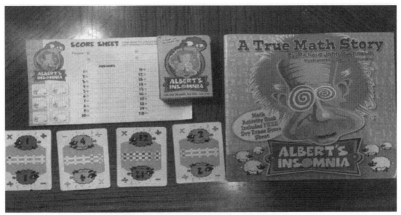

Albert's Insomnia: The Teacher's Kit

James Tanton: In Praise of Professionals

My charge: Teach polynomial division to high-schoolers. My reaction: Why?

—James Tanton

Dr. James Tanton has what I (Chris) consider to be the best job title in the world, mathematician at large for the Mathematical Association of America. First, a little background. Tanton is Australian born but now lives in Arizona in the United States. He is a Princeton-educated PhD and also a founding member of the Global Math Project (GMP), for which Sunil and I are both ambassadors. His work takes him all over the world as a supporter of mathematical education efforts. Before this role, however, after he graduated from Princeton, he wanted to teach. He became a high-school mathematics teacher. Below we retell his story of how he developed the Exploding Dots idea that has become the core of the GMP's mission. This is where the story picks up:

> The quote at the top of this chapter sets the scene for the genesis of Exploding Dots. If you are unaware of what polynomial division is, basically it is the long division of algebraic expressions by other algebraic expressions. In case you don't recall it from your school days, this subject is more than a tad abstract, though not too abstract to a person well versed in Algebra, which James was at the time. The question "Why?" is not a hands-in-the-air, attempt at covering his lack of understanding of "how to do the math" ; no, it was a serious question, and one that all teachers of mathematics ought to ask themselves about each and every piece of content they choose to include in their curriculum (and no, "because the standards say I have to" is not a good enough reason).

But back to James. He was genuinely struggling with the purpose of this subject's inclusion in his class. He kept his question private, though. "I knew the system I was in—the high-school math education system—and the expectations of that system, namely, to teach a rigid collection of algorithms and mathematical techniques that have been the standard curriculum norm for over a century..." He had been hired to teach secondary mathematics in a school in an eastern state in the United States, and he was aware that this system had a long history of choosing what constituted the content of math classes through tradition often with indefensible choices, usually with little thought as to that fundamental question, "Why?" He had asked around, wondering aloud what others thought about the reason for including this subject and the "three least vague reasons" he had heard were:

1. We teach students these things because they will need to know them later on.
2. Because colleges expect students to know these things.
3. Mathematics is a great tool for teaching thinking and deep problem-solving.

He told me that while he was a graduate of one of the top mathematics research institutions on the planet, he had to wrack his brain as to what the phrase "polynomial division" even meant. He couldn't recall ever needing to divide two polynomials, ever, in all his years of research. He could remember working with a mathematical construct called a "ring," but only about 0.001 percent of humanity will ever need to think much about them. First reason down the tubes.

What about reason two? James described to me that while working in a liberal arts college environment, he never heard any of his colleagues lamenting, "Oh I do wish these students could divide polynomials better!"—not once. However, there was general consensus regarding a lack of understanding of why algorithms worked, where they came from, and what human understanding is caught up in developing them. This seemed a far more important set of goals to him and his colleagues. So, reason number two, out the window with you!

James then turned his thinking to reason number three—math is a great tool for teaching thinking and deep problem-solving. He wonders how this is pushed forward by teaching polynomial division by this method known as synthetic division, a very mysterious method indeed. (I have taught mathematics to high-school teachers for some eighteen years now, and I have never heard any of them give a good explanation for why it works or how it does its job.) The process is, in James' words, "...an almighty opaque bit of quite bizarre twists and turns through a table of mysterious construction..." This is the case, and what's worse is we are expected to teach it as nothing more than a bare set of algorithmic steps, steps whose connections are shrouded in a cloud of unknowing. To the point, the expectation is to teach this without providing reasons, or to encourage thinking at all. So the third reason is shot. And to make matters worse, all the answers that could be gotten in this method are found far more easily using Google or some other ubiquitous technology. It could in fact be argued that teaching polynomial division through the synthetic division process is training students NOT to think effectively but rather to be mindless processors not caring a bit about what it is they do.

James tells of examining the math curriculum firsthand and having what I think Sunil would agree is a Paul Lockhart moment. This is the situation people with love and great affinity for a subject find themselves in when they see what textbooks have done to it. Lockhart came to this place, and it drove him to write that first essay and later the book, *A Mathematician's Lament*. James was in this same sort of place and described to me in a letter that this idea (mathematics) that he so passionately loved had been "...broken down into small, miniscule chunks, jumbled about and conducted in isolation in such a way as to strip away any sense of human or mathematical story. Focusing on algorithm mastery and speed, with no room for play, flailing, innovating, thinking, or questioning." He looked out at a curriculum devoid of humanness, humor, or joy.

His charge, nonetheless, was to teach polynomial division. What to do?

Enter Exploding Dots

After looking closely at this process, James asks, "So what is the storyline of this desire to divide polynomials, whatever they are?" Well, polynomials are an abstraction of the numbers we have been dividing since fifth grade, and humans have found good reason to do division for many millennia now. Dealing with quantity and amount, representing it, manipulating it, and sharing and distributing amounts of goods have been essential human tasks since we banded together in small groups and divided up labor to assist each other.

Before I go too deep into the story of how Exploding Dots was developed and a bit of how it works, let me give you a few sentences on what they do. Exploding Dots represents numbers as dots in a long line of boxes. When any box gets a given number of dots in it (say ten), the user (you) can "explode those ten dots and make them reappear in the box to the left as one single dot. That's it in a nutshell. This process and adherence to logic make all the operations (addition, subtraction, multiplication, division, etc.) work. Of course, as with all sorts of games, once you set some rules down, the fun begins with examining the consequences of those rules. When life gives you choices, be prepared: It always asks you to deal with the consequences—a great life lesson.

Humans have developed ways of writing and representing numbers (quantities, amounts) that also provide us with convenient means to manipulate them. This actually has taken us vast millennia to accomplish. That numbering did not come down from above as a fully formed system is testified to in history and fossil records. There are archaeological finds more than one hundred thousand years old in which humans have recorded quantities in bones and other hard surfaces as records of quantities. Today we don't make scratch marks in bone to keep records; rather, we use a sophisticated numeration system that has traced its history from the Indian subcontinent, through the Fertile Crescent, Mediterranean Europe, the Americas, and the rest of the developed world.

We presently use ten-ness as a primary means of grouping quantities. James tells of realizing that this too is an arbitrary choice we have made, and we could have, and in fact some cultures have, developed a different number to base our system on. Ten seems a "handy" choice, though, with its ten "digits," including a 0. In our system, the number 555 might use the same digit over and over again, but because of each one's location a different value is associated with it. For instance, if you read that number out loud you can hear the value of the "place" each 5 is in in your words. Five "hundred" five-ty (sometimes pronounced fifty, though we can't figure out why) five.

On top of this, because all these operations obey the laws of mathematics, they can be done in all sorts of crazy orders without breaking the deep rules of mathematics. There may be good reasons for going right to left in an addition problem, but those reasons are *not* because "*you have to!*" You can add middle numbers together first if you like, or multiply from left to right, even divide without ever breaking out that sideways L shape where you put one number "inside" and another "outside." These are not *have to* rules; they are just conventions we have adopted. This knowledge is what moved James forward. Mathematics doesn't care about what number it is based on; it could be sloth (base six), human (base ten), or Martian (base eight). I have it on good authority that Martians have four digits per hand. James' wife is an astronomer, so you can trust me on this one.). Thinking through these realities, James realized that he can do this in any base he wants, and even better, he can do mathematics in *all* bases at the same time by simply leaving the base number a mystery for a while and calling it *x*. When he does this, he has moved into the world of polynomials, where he wanted to be all along, because the curriculum told him he had to, and James may be iconoclastic, but he does not necessarily seek out rule breaking.

In the picture on the following page, you can see how Exploding Dots with polynomials behaves exactly like dividing with natural numbers. With this insight, James has all he needs to solve his problem. He builds lessons around using these dots that explode

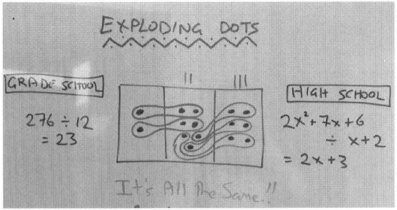

Here is an example how Exploding Dots reveals that algebra and arithmetic are one idea. It is just the case that in algebra the base you are working in is as yet unknown to you, and immaterial.

in organized manner on whiteboards in any base he wants. He can demonstrate the operations in mathematics with these dots within these "machines" he claims to have invented when he was "just a lad." These dots and their antithesis "tods" can be incorporated to create a robust arithmetic in any base and allow the user to accompany all their calculations with sound effects and laughter. You will never enter a room where children are doing mathematics using Exploding Dots where you will not also hear "Kaboom!" "Kapow!" or "Pfffft" accompanying shouts of "I get it!" "The answer is 23!" and "OH MY GOODNESS! I NEVER KNEW THAT!" (this last one comes most often when showing teachers Exploding Dots). Playfulness and joy are abundant in these settings.

Global Math Project

Back to James Tanton, mathematical evangelist. As I mentioned earlier, he travels the world describing the joys of Exploding Dots and other mathematical wonders. In 2015 or so, he and a small group of other enthusiasts set for themselves the task of giving mathematics a social facelift of sorts. It seems that not all people experience joy or playfulness when doing math (hence this book). Just before this brainstorming, Code.org had launched its successful Hour of Code campaign to encourage children and adults to do an hour of computer coding to illustrate the simple joy of making a machine do the work you want it to and therefore demystifying computer programming. James and his colleagues began to dream of accomplishing the same thing with mathematics.

The group members eventually formed what is now known as the Global Math Project. They set a target date of October 10, 2017 as their launch, and a goal of getting some joyful and uplifting mathematics in the hands of one million students by the end of the first week, October 17, 2017. It was an audacious and intimidating goal. There are 1.2 billion school-aged children in the world, and while reaching one million of them was a small drop in that bucket, it was still a huge number.

The Global Math Project has, as James told me, "... proved the worldwide hunger for and wonder at the universal, human story that is mathematics." One of the first events that got things going was that James made a presentation at the National Council of Teachers of Mathematics conference in 2016. There he recruited his first group of ambassadors to North America, and then the GMP team enlisted the help of Scolab, a software development team in Canada. Scolab went on to develop GMP's web-based application, which is available for free to all, in perpetuity. Through much work, some sweat, and maybe even a few tears of frustration, the first annual Global Math Week kicked off on October 10, 2017, and before midnight (EDT), the number of official registrants crossed the one million mark. By the end of the week, roughly 1.7 million students had registered and engaged in Exploding Dots at some level.

In October 2018 for the second annual Global Math Week, the number of students positively impacted by the inclusion of Exploding Dots in their curriculum reached beyond 5 million. It continues to grow, and plans are already underway for the third annual Global Math Week. From the humble beginnings of a conscientious professional asking a simple question about, "Why is this in the curriculum?" grew a movement to impact the world. Five million students are no small impact. In speaking with James, he is still not content with this; you get the sense that he will not rest until all the world sees what he sees: "Mathematics is a joyous, uplifting, audacious, bold, wonder-filled, and playful human endeavor!"

Marjorie Rice: In Awe of Amateurs

We decided to include this story of Marjorie Rice because it underscores the fact that many of us are just mathematicians waiting to be born, and that wait might extend well beyond our schooling years. This story is adapted from a 2018 article written by Doris Schattschneider that appeared in the *Journal of Mathematics and the Arts*.

If you look at the image here of a floor, you might notice that it is beautiful but complicated. And if you walked across it you might pay it no attention at all. But how it came to be is a fascinating and wonderful story of a person who played with mathematics for fun and no other reason. Marjorie Rice is probably not a name you have heard before. Her story is rich with all the ideas we hope to inspire with this book.

The picture in this chapter is of a floor that is also of Marjorie's design. I had the opportunity to see, photograph, and walk on it in the summer of 2018. I have not been to the Mathematical Association of America (MAA)'s building to see the original. What is pictured is in front of a beautiful museum of technology and science in Stockholm, Sweden.

This tile pattern is outside the Tekniska Museet (Museum of Technology) in Stockholm, Sweden. It is a reflection (and a more colorful interpretation) of the same pattern used by the Mathematical Association of America, created by Marjorie Rice. Photo taken by Chris Brownell in July 2018.

Rice's story relative to this floor begins in 1975. She was a fifty-two-year-old full-time homemaker living in San Diego and raising five children. Her husband was self-employed and owned his own printing business in town. She had purchased a subscription to *Scientific American,* which was a monthly periodical that updated the general reader on discoveries and breakthroughs in science. The subscription, however, was not for her but rather for her son, who loved science.

Rice had been raised in an era when women were not typically encouraged to study math or science; in fact, she had taken only one math course in high school and had decided to go to secretarial school. The truth was, however, that she had been an avid reader of Martin Gardner's *Mathematical Games* columns in the *Scientific American* magazine for years. I picture her sneaking into her son's room when he was at school, sitting on his bed and thumbing through the periodical, skipping the articles on advances in biology, seeking the real attraction, the treasure trove that was this regular column. As she sat, alone in a big house, kids at school and husband at work, she would pull out a pad of paper and scribble notes and ideas about various puzzles, perhaps making her own M.C. Escher–type drawings—all unbeknownst to her family.

Then, in 1975, she read in one of Gardner's columns about the debunking of a previous claim from a man named Robert Kershner. Five months earlier he had claimed to have shown that he had found ALL eight of the tessellating pentagons that could possibly exist. This new article reported that a gentleman named Richard James had found one more.

These ideas struck a deep chord with Rice. Something intrigued her enough to get out her notebook and get to work. She had a keen sense of organization—perhaps from her training as a secretary. or perhaps it was innate—but no formal mathematical training and no formal means to make and keep notes or any standard nomenclature for the task. She had to invent her own method.

Rice's method turned out to be a stroke of brilliance. She created a system of pictorial descriptions of what she was reading in Gardner's column. In a nutshell, there are a few invariant truths to this problem: First, the sum of all angles inside a pentagon always add up to 540 degrees; second, where two or more pentagons meet to completely encircle a point, the angles of the pentagons must add up to 360 degrees.

She also noticed that in any pentagonal tiling, the angles of the pentagons would have to occur an equal number of times. This led her to a discovery about the original eight from Kershner—that two of them had angles that occurred twice. She then set about to make a list of the twelve ways in which you could pair angles of a pentagon and their corresponding angle sums. Rice literally exhausted all possibilities of combinations—something Kershner and James had not done. She classified these twelve ways into one of three categories: Impossible, Possible and Known, and Possible but New.

She then set out to create some small template triangles and modify them to see if they could work. She worked essentially in secret, testing her theories again and again in the quiet moments when her husband was at work and her children were at school. By February 1976, she was certain she had found a new pentagon that would tile the plane, one that neither Kershner nor James had discovered. She sent several sketches to Gardner. He didn't know what to make of them, so he sent them to several mathematicians he consulted when he struggled. One of those mathematicians was Doris Schattschneider, a PhD in mathematics who was on the faculty at Moravian College; she is now retired. She is the only one who saw Rice's nonstandard notation as holding accurate information and confirmed that this was indeed a *new* tiling. Her acknowledgment sparked the beginning of a twenty-five-year friendship and collaboration between the two women. Schattschneider would become Rice's champion and work with her across decades.

It took until 1988 for Gardner to publish Rice's discoveries in *Scientific American*. This meant that she had discovered type ten. In the ensuing years, however, she turned her eyes to a slightly different permutation of the problem from the one in which she made her original discovery. She went on to create a whole new class of pentagonal tilings based on her discovery that every double hexagon can be divided into four pentagons, and therefore pentagons can be formed into tilings that are nested in the double hexagons. This discovery proved very fruitful.

"I could hardly keep up with all the material she sent me," Schattschneider wrote in the article for the *Journal of Mathematics and the Arts*. The double hexagon connection led Rice to types eleven, twelve, and thirteen, the last of which Schattschneider described as coming to her in "a large packet of material that showed 103 different arrangements…" Rice became relentless in her pursuit of finding all the tilings. She sought them out in what is called a "combinatorial search," which is to say that she tried to investigate every single possible class of pentagons.

Her story goes on for twenty-five years, with huge discoveries and new and interesting methods of coloring and painting pentagonal tilings to look like Escher drawings, several of which now hang in museums. In 1993 Rice received a copy of a computer tool called "Reptiles" to generate tessellations, and this gave her a new way to investigate. It also moved her closer to a method for investigating the 4,300 different varieties of "convex" pentagons that might tile the plane.

By the end of her life, Rice had discovered six new classes of convex pentagons (since then another has been added) and some 103 classes of concave pentagons that tile the plane. In 1998 the MAA was seeking an interesting tiling pattern for its new building. A famous mathematician had only recently published a work on what is known as a Penrose tiling (an aperiodic tiling made with two different quadrilaterals that looks patterned but ends up being chaotic over large scale). This was a natural choice, but then Doris Schattschneider suggested Marjorie Rice's number fifty-six tiling, because it was quite unique and discovered by an amateur. The MAA agreed, and that is the tile pattern mentioned at the beginning of this story.

Epilogue: Throughout most of those twenty-five years, Rice kept her discoveries fairly quiet, eschewing publicity to the extent that her family didn't necessarily recognize the significance of the findings and contributions she made. One day Schattschneider was going to deliver a paper on the codiscoveries she and Rice had made in the field. She had persuaded Rice to attend the talk, and though she agreed, Rice refused to go before the crowd to be recognized, still believing she hadn't done much. After the lunch break during these meetings, and after Schattschneider had given her talk, she told the gathered collection of mathematicians in a large conference room, "I have a very special guest with me today. Ladies and gentlemen, Marjorie Rice sits here in the front row." Rice stood, and the room erupted in a standing ovation that lasted much longer than might be expected. With her husband beside her, the housewife, mother of five, and discoverer of a multitude was honored by some of the most accomplished mathematicians in the world for the contributions she had made to the field. Imagining that scene never fails to bring a lump to my throat and tears to my eyes. In fact, I have to stop writing to collect myself, pardon me a moment...

One last thought—anyone who says that mathematics is a cold, hard, and inhuman study is absolutely mistaken, and I feel as bad for them as I am thrilled for Marjorie Rice. Her story is not merely one of a young woman being pigeonholed into a secretarial position because of her gender, but of a curriculum sorely lacking in creative opportunities for all students to encounter mathematics.

Although there are thousands of stories still to be told, I believe that there is no better story to champion the idea of who is a mathematician than the story of Marjorie Rice. And, to end it on Chris sharing—releasing—his own personal moment about the story, well, we should close this chapter, but hopefully open so many more about the stories in mathematics…

QUESTIONS FOR DEEPER DISCUSSION

1. How can you use the power of stories and storytelling to engage your students in a more playful experience with mathematics?

2. How can you create a learning environment that will keep the next Marjorie Rice from falling through the cracks? How can you nurture her love of mathematics?

3. Mathematical history is punctuated by very human people, and their creations and discoveries are colored by who they were at the time they made them. How does thinking about math as a subject in the humanities alter what you teach and how you teach it?

> *There is no greater agony than bearing*
> *an untold story inside of you.*

—Maya Angelou

CHAPTER 7

Mind Blown

This chapter provides some instances of mathematical truths that, quite frankly, give both of us reason to pause and just say, WOW! These truths might provide insight into the twisted minds of the two people who wrote the words you are reading, but we also hope they help you enjoy the experience of having your mind completely blown! This said, some readers might not be as intrigued by these complex ideas, so feel free to skip over those that are not interesting to you. There is no quiz at the end, and none of this will be on next week's test.

> ### *The moments of happiness we enjoy take us by surprise. It is not that we seize them, but that they seize us.*
>
> —Ashley Montague

Chris was kind enough to add a note to the landscape of this chapter, which at times will be bumpy and exhausting. As any good adventure, some of the best stories are those that at times were bewildering or overwhelming. This chapter was not written for teachers with high levels of knowledge or even an interest in mathematics, although, on the surface, it might appear that way. No. It was written for everyone, in hopes that even one of these ideas might trigger the dormant spirit of longing for the *sea of mathematics.*

If you want to build a ship, don't drum up people to collect wood and don't assign them tasks and work, but rather teach them to long for the endless immensity of the sea.

Antoine de Saint-Exupéry

One of the most innovative, optimistic, and kind-hearted math educators I know is Maria Droujkova, the director of naturalmath. com. Droujkova approaches the learning of mathematics with the deep empathy and kindness of an elementary teacher yet through a long K–12 lens. She sees even a high school topic like calculus as one that can be visually and joyfully unpacked by five-year-olds. Maybe we have it wrong. Instead of seeing the most challenging ideas through older and confident eyes, perhaps the key to it all is seeing them through the unjaded eyes of a child.

As elementary teachers know far too well, children listen to stories. The bigger the story the better. The only difference is that the stories in mathematics are all *nonfiction*. The intent and final meaning of this chapter is perhaps best explained through a story I told my ten-year-old daughter on December 21, 2018. I mention the date, because it was another milestone date for mathematics—the date the fifty-first Mersenne prime was found. Even if you know what a Mersenne prime is, you should be severely doubting the point of transmitting this information to a young child whose primary interests are unicorns, Minecraft, experimenting with nail polish, and her dog. At the same time, she's a kid who has also become magically transfixed by prime numbers.

It was shortly after dinner, and I was mildly consumed with how best to convey this chapter to readers. I really wanted its message—*math is for everyone*—to come through with clarity and conviction. In my Facebook feed, the news that the fifty-first Mersenne prime number was found (after two weeks of verification) came across. Sitting beside me was my daughter. She was watching an episode of *Fuller House*. I wasn't sure if I could successfully convey what a Mersenne prime is and its importance to my happily preoccupied daughter, but I gave it a try. I asked her, "Raya, do you want to know something cool about prime numbers?" She said, "Sure, Popsicle!" (My kids call me Poppi, and my daughter likes to call me Pops or Popsicle.)

I first showed her what a Mersenne prime is, using the stamp below, to plant the seed of its importance. It was discovered in 1963, and it was the twenty-third Mersenne prime ever discovered.

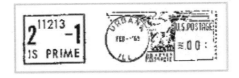

Raya had no idea what an exponent was. I told her a Mersenne prime always looks "like this," and I asked her to give me a random number. She said ten, and I wrote:

$$2^{10} - 1$$

First, I taught her to pronounce it correctly—"two to the exponent ten minus one." We practiced saying it a few times. I then told her that this configuration is the equivalent of multiplying the number 2 ten times, adding that that the ten is "shouting instructions" down to the 2 in terms of how many times it needs to multiply itself. She giggled. Then immediately reached for her inexpensive dollar store calculator. She punched in the number 2, tapped the multiplication sign ten times, and 1,024 came up. We subtracted 1 and got 1,023. I asked her whether it was a prime number. I shrugged my shoulders. We decided to break it down, and sure enough, 1,023 was not prime.

It is actually:

$$3 \times 11 \times 31$$

Next, we tried smaller numbers, starting with 1 and going to 5:

$$2^1 - 1 = 1$$
$$2^2 - 1 = 3$$
$$2^3 - 1 = 7$$
$$2^4 - 1 = 15$$
$$2^5 - 1 = 31$$

Raya was excited to see so many primes generated by this new idea and new structure of numbers. She also quickly pointed out that 1 and 15 are not prime. I then told her the fifty-first Mersenne prime was just announced today. She was polite but not terribly enthusiastic. That all changed when she saw the *size* of the exponent. I asked her to write it out to feel the magnitude. A simple task that nurtures curiosity and a future anticipation of the next one. Showing as many nuggets of mathematical gold to students will amplify a lifetime treasure hunt for more.

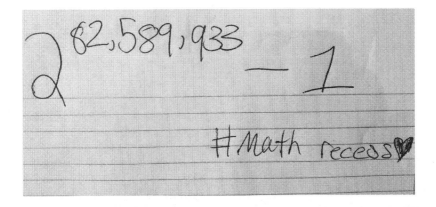

Innocently enough, she went back to her calculator, and started tapping the multiplication sign with the input of 2. After twenty-eight taps, her calculator conked out with the word "overflow." I told her even if you had a calculator powerful enough—and a big enough display—it would take you about eight months of tapping to generate this prime number. She was speechless, impressed, and her mind was blown!

By now you surely must know—*we hope you know*—that the end game of mathematics must orbit around the most majestic and head-spinning ideas for all of our students. It must be more than "mathematics for all." It must be "*all* mathematics for all."

We must be consumed by this. But this consumption will not drain us. It will revive us and lead us to a love of mathematics that demands to be shared.

Sunil Singh
@Mathgarden

Children don't hate math.
What they hate is being
confused, intimidated, and
embarrassed by math.
With understanding
comes passion, and with
passion comes growth - a
treasure is unlocked.

Larry Martinek

7:44 am - 19 Aug 2018

900 Retweets 2,374 Likes

On a Sunday morning in August 2018, I tweeted a post about children and mathematics. I post stuff like this all the time, but as you can see by the numbers, this one went viral. These twenty-eight words reverberated powerfully for weeks. The emotive key to unlocking mathematical treasures was found. Thousands of people agreed. There are many ways to instill this passion. They can come from deep and long dives into mathematical ideas. They also can come from sudden, often surprising, ideas about mathematics.

While we have picked the ideas below for their WOW factor, we also want to make sure that underlying all of this is some fundamental mathematics in multiplication that gets extended into things like factorials, exponentiation, and beyond! The best place to practice basic skills are in the arenas of the wildly imaginative—to extend yourself as far as you can go. You might not make it the first time, but you will come back. You will want to come back.

Prime Numbers

- Twenty-five percent of numbers from 1 to 100 are prime. Only 7.9 percent of numbers from 1 to 1,000,000 are prime. The idea that they grow less and less *popular* as you go further and further out has fascinated mathematicians, both amateur and professional alike, for thousands of years.
- The largest prime number found by hand, in 1876, after nineteen years of testing by Édouard Lucas, has thirty-nine digits. The first largest prime found by computer, in 1951, has seventy-nine digits. The largest known prime number, found in 2017, has 23,249,425 digits.
- An emirp is a prime number that stays prime after reversing its digits (e.g., 37 → 73).
- There are seventeen ways to write 17 as a sum of prime numbers.
- The following numbers are all prime:
  331
  3,331
  33,331
  333,331
  3,333,331
  33,333,331

Sigh. This unusual pattern stops at 333,333,331, which is not prime, because it's 17 × 19,607,843, which is interesting because at seventeen Chris was a ski bum who had been born in 1960, had graduated high school in '78, and he went on to first hear of this number at age 43. (OK, maybe not so interesting.)

- Another strange prime is 73,939,133. If you keep removing one digit at a time from the right, the resulting numbers stay prime—73,939,13 and 73,939,1 and 73,939 and 7,393 and 739 and 73 and 7 are all prime!

This article written in *Medium* has even more quirky ideas about primes.

Prime Spirals, Five Guys Facts
bit.do/mathrecess-primes

Mr. E's Infinitude

[SMP: 3] I am placing the statement of which SMP: this addresses at the top of the next section. The reason for that is the SMP: addressed is #3: "Construct viable arguments and critique the reasoning of others." What follows is a paraphrase of an argument; it would not be included in a mathematical journal because it would not meet the standards for a rigorous proof that they set. It is, in Chris' opinion, however, a "viable" argument. Please feel free to critique it. One other important thing to note, the argument presented here relies on a form that can seem misleading. We make a statement that has exactly two alternatives (there are or are not an infinite number of primes). Then we will assume that one of the alternatives (there are an infinite number of primes), which we want to prove true, is false (there is a largest prime number), then through a series of linked syllogisms demonstrate that our assumption must be false (there cannot be a largest prime number); therefore, what we wanted to prove true must be the only true alternative.

Euclid's proof of what is known as the Infinitude of the Primes (the provable fact that there must be an infinite number of prime numbers) is certainly mind-blowing. At the same time, some people see it and think, *Duh. I could have thought that up had I put my mind to it.* It makes use of one of the oldest tricks in the mathematician's playbook. In Latin it is known as *reductio ad absurdum*, which loosely translated to English is "reducing to an absurdity." Euclid, or Mr. E. for short (say it fast and you'll get it), the world's first geometry textbook writer, makes a claim that he plans to show is absurd in the end. He states his claim in such a way that either it is true, or if it is shown to be false, the opposite of the claim has to be true.

Mr. E's absurd claim: There is a largest prime number.

Simple, right? Let's follow his plan and dress it up in some modern thinking. Because there is a largest prime number, we can give it a name. James, Keith, and Marjorie all are fine candidates, but they take too long to write out, so let's call it L. To be clear, L is the largest number that has no factors besides 1 and itself. This means there are no other numbers past L, to the right on the number line, that have this property. Pause a moment and be sure you grasp this little point before moving on, because it is key.

Let's take a little detour for a moment. I would like to point out that if you multiply the whole numbers, say from 1 to 5, the answer, the product, is divisible by every single number between 1 and 5. Take a moment to think on this. To illustrate what I mean, consider multiplying out $1 \times 2 \times 3 \times 4 \times 5$ and you will get 120. Does it make sense that 120 is divisible by 1, 2, 3, 4, and 5? Furthermore, it doesn't matter where you end; the product will always be divisible by all the whole numbers less than the whole number you stopped at.

> A tiny mathematical aside. When mathematicians want to think about something like 1 X 2 X 3 X 4 they don't want to have to write it all out, so they invented a simple and compact notation for it. That notation uses an "!" after a number to mean that multiplication. So 4! Is not an excited 4 but it means 4 X 3 X 2 X 1. But neatly, think of all the writing that saves if you want to think of 100! *Wow!*

One last little turn on this short detour. Consider adding 1 to the answer of that product. Using our previous example, we would add 1 to 120—the product of 1 through 5—which gives you 121. Please notice that, except for 1, none of the other numbers—2, 3, 4, or 5— divide evenly into 121. (Another way to think about this is that to find the next number after 120 divisible by 2, we'd have to add 2 to the product, and to find the next number divisible by 3, we'd have to add 3 to the product, to find the next number divisible by 4, and so on. So when we just add 1, we will make a number that is not divisible by any of the numbers used in the multiplication that got us 120.) This is the case no matter where we stop. Here we just multiplied from 1 through 5 then added 1 to find a number not divisible by any of the numbers 2 through 5. This same sort of thing would happen if we multiply 1 through 17 (or any whole number you like) and then add 1. There will always be a remainder of 1 when you divide by the whole numbers less than the biggest in the list.

Now back to Mr. E's absurd claim. Before taking our detour, we had named the largest prime L. Consider what happens when we multiply $1 \times 2 \times 3 \times 4 \times 5 \ldots \times L$. As you can imagine, this will be an extremely large number. We are looking at L! Right? (See the inserted box above) We know from our detour that all the whole numbers less than L will divide evenly into L! We also know that none of them will divide evenly into L! + 1. This leaves us with two options for what L! + 1 looks like:

L! + 1 is an immense number that has some number that is between L and it that divides into it evenly; or

L! + 1 has no numbers greater than L that divide into it evenly.

That's it, those two options are all we have. Look carefully at both of these, and you will see that both of them require the existence of some prime number greater than L to exist; do you see it? But Mr. E claims that L is the *largest* prime of them all. This is *absurd*! We have no choice but to reject Mr. E's claim that there is a largest prime... therefore, there are an infinite number of primes. *AHHHHHHhhhhh* so satisfying to use our brains in play. [SMP: 3, 7]

The Pigeonhole Principle

The pigeonhole principle is a powerful tool used in combinatorial math. The idea is simple and can be explained by the following peculiar problem. Imagine that three pigeons need to be placed into two pigeonholes. Can it be done? The answer is yes, but there is one catch. The catch is that no matter how the pigeons are placed, one of the pigeonholes must contain more than one pigeon.

The logic can be generalized for larger numbers. The pigeonhole principle states that if more than n pigeons are placed into n pigeonholes, some pigeonhole must contain more than one pigeon. While the principle is evident, its implications are astounding. The reason is that the principle proves the existence or impossibility of a particular phenomenon.

- For every twenty-seven-word sequence in any book, at least two words will start with the same letter. There are twenty-seven words or "pigeons" that can start with one of the twenty-six different English letters or "pigeonholes." By the pigeonhole principle, two of the words must start with the same letter.
- In Toronto, there are two nonbald people who have the same number of hairs on their head. The human head can contain up to several hundred thousand hairs, with a maximum of about five hundred thousand. That means that of the millions of people in Toronto, at least two of them must share the same number of hairs.
- The famous "sock" problems are all based on the pigeonhole principle! Try this one.

In your bedroom, you have a drawer with many socks—two red, four yellow, six purple, eight brown, ten white, twelve green, fourteen black, sixteen blue, eighteen gray, and twenty orange socks. It is dark, so you cannot tell what colors the socks are. What is the fewest number of socks you need to take out of the drawer before you must get a matching pair? (*Hint: Just focus on the colors.*) For younger classes, we suggest with starting only three colors. Ask your students to come up with their own pigeonhole problems and make a collage.

Factorials

Six weeks lasts exactly 10! seconds. This is a cool idea that will help students see factorial notation through some nifty time conversion. For the purposes of demonstrating this, 3 will be written as $\sqrt{9}$.

> $3 \times 4 \times 5$ seconds in a minute
> 6×10 minutes in an hour
> $8 \times \sqrt{9}$ hours in a day
> 7 days in a week
> $2* \sqrt{9}$ weeks in six weeks.

(Explanation: $\sqrt{9}$ is 3, and $\sqrt{9} \times \sqrt{9} = 9$, so you end up with $1 \times 2 \times 3 \times 4 \times 5 \times 6 \times 7 \times 8 \times 9 \times 10$, which is 10!).

Follow this up with this question: How old in years do you have to be to have lived a billion seconds? It doesn't require factorials, but it is a way cool idea.

Deck of Cards

We think card games are pretty limited because there are only 52 cards, but it's ridiculous how many combinations you have in these 52 cards. There are, of course, 52! possible combinations Crazy factorial! To unpack this number...

80658175170943878571660636856403766975289505
44088327782400000000000000.

That number is beyond astronomically large, but that's exactly how many ways you can arrange fifty-two cards. Remember that when you're shuffling a deck! Shuffle it properly—you might create a completely new arrangement, one that no one has ever created before.

Primes

The only factorial that is a prime is 2!, which equals $1 \times 2 = 2$. However, there are many primes that are just one above or one below the factorial numbers! Keep in mind that any factorial number past 69! is bigger than Googol, which has on hundred 0s!

n! + 1 is prime for n = 0, 1, 2, 3, 11, 27, 37, 41, 73, 77
n! − 1 is prime for n = 3, 4, 6, 7, 12, 14, 30, 32, 33, 38, 94

Brown Numbers

A curious relationship exists between factorials and square numbers. It goes like this:

$$m^2 = n! + 1$$

For example, two numbers (m, n) that satisfy this equation are (5, 4). Are there more? Surprisingly, not too many more. To be specific, only two more! They would be (11, 5) and (71, 7). Isn't math wonderfully weird? We think so!

Ramsey Numbers

Back in Chapter 2, we explored a pencil game called Nim. It is directly related to a particular number called the Ramsey Number. The number that the game of Nim represents is:

R (3, 3) = 6

A wonderful video that illustrates the basis for this number is found below.

Can you solve the time travel riddle?, Dan Finkel
bit.do/mathrecess8

We are going to switch from this problem to something more human and call it the "Party Problem." Already sounds more fun! What the above number represents is that when you have a room of six people, it is guaranteed—yes, guaranteed—that there will be at least one smaller group of three people who will all be friends or all be strangers. That makes sense because in our Nim game we were guaranteed that somebody would end up drawing a triangle with all the same color sides. So, for example, red could mean "friend" and blue could mean "stranger." There will be a triangle (three people) that will be either all red or all blue.

That is not the mind-blown part.

What do you think R (4, 4) equals? How many people must be at the party to guarantee that there will be a group of four people (in which all six connections between them) are all friends or all strangers to one another? The answer turns out to be eighteen. Once you have that many people in the room, you will be guaranteed to have this clique of four people who are either all friends or all strangers! A fatiguing exercise would be to draw a circle with eighteen points all around. Connect every point with all the other ones using two colors and try avoiding using all colors for any set of four points. Or, you can just trust us!

That is not the mind-blown part.

R (2, 2) = 2. Which is kind of trivial. When there are only two people in the room, they are either friends or strangers. R (3, 3) = 6, a hexagonal arrangement. R (4, 4) = 18. What do you think R (5, 5) is equal to? Many people say 54, because the answers seem to be multiplying by 3. This is a very valid observation, and a decent guess. However, the answer is lower. 50? Lower. 45?

Maybe.

Maybe? Since when in mathematics do you get a *maybe*? You sometimes know the answer for sure or have no clue, but this wishy-washy *maybe*? Yup. Nobody has figured out the answer yet, but mathematicians have figured out the lower and upper bounds, thinking that the answer lies between 43 and 49. Imagine a question that can be easily understood by elementary kids—it has to do with making friends—and quickly spirals into the unknowing, with numbers that are less than 50!

In 1990, the famous Paul Erdos said this about the elusive R(5, 5):

> Suppose aliens invade the earth and threaten to obliterate it in a year's time unless human beings can find the Ramsey number for red 5 and blue 5. We could marshal the world's best minds and fastest computers, and within a year we could probably calculate the value. If the aliens demanded the Ramsey number for

red 6 and blue 6, however, we would have no choice
but to launch a preemptive attack.

Basically, what he was saying was that it would be a better strategy
to try and defeat the aliens than take on the behemoth task of going
after R (6, 6).

Graham's Number

It is no small wonder that a problem involving the impossibility of
solving a Ramsey Number situation with alien invasion involves one of
the most legendary numbers in the history of mathematics—Graham's
number. It is a number so large that the cheeky folks at Numberphile
jokingly believe that your brain can turn into a black hole by thinking
about it too long. That somehow your brain will not so much be mind
blown, but more like undergo implosion because of the density of
thinking that is involved in imagining Graham's Number.

We are going to omit the actual problem Ron Graham posed in
the 1970s. Loosely, it involves coloring edges with two colors and
vertices. And of course, ending up in the thirteenth dimension. *Of
course.* We are going to *try* and explain and build Graham's Number.
Heck, we will probably fail, but we are going to give it a go!

Actually, inasmuch there is an earnest task to walk you through
the enormity of this number, we actually don't expect too many of
you to hang on and make it to the gargantuan end. I know both Chris
and I succumb early to the massiveness of Graham's. But that is kind
of the point. Where does it get overwhelming for you? When does
your head explode? When do you realize that mathematics has the
ability to crush everyone—and that we can all laugh about it? Lack
of comprehension doesn't always have to wear such a dour badge.
Sometimes it makes us mortal. And that's okay.

In April of 2014, Evelyn Lamb (@evelynjlamb) wrote an absolutely monster of a piece regarding Graham's Number. Not only was it wonderfully on point, but it was written with wry humor, to preface the futility of explaining Graham's Number. The title of her *Scientific American* article was sheer genius, and the accompanying subtitle was equally stellar.

Graham's Number Is Too Big for Me to Tell You How Big It Is

I was going to write an April Fool's Day post with the title "Mathematicians Declare Graham's Number Equal to Infinity." Graham's number is really big, but of course, it's precisely 0% as big as infinity.

By Evelyn Lamb on April 1, 2014

In the article, Lamb talks about some big numbers we know like Googol. It's a good starting point. Then there is mention of Googolplex, which is 10^{Googol} or a 1 followed by a Googol number of 0s. Now, even though this number is a number most of us would consider rather beastly, at least this number can be imagined for its length. You cannot write out this number on a piece of paper—even if that paper was the size of the observable universe and we wrote each digit the size of a Planck length (the smallest unit of measure that we know).

In terms of Planck lengths, the universe is 1061 in diameter across. Do you see the problem? Googolplex is 10100. And, because this is exponentiation, although 61 as an exponent might seem close, it is anything but. Even with this impossible shrinkage of writing, we would only be

0.0000000000000000000000000000001 percent of the way to writing it. What about atoms? There are 10^{80} of those. Far from close and no cigar! The universe is too small to write out Googolplex. And, as frustrating as that is, *we at least understand our frustration.* With Graham's number there is no such consolation, only frustration, exasperation, and then, a sane exit, with maybe a "what the hell was that?"

Because Lamb's is the best explanation I have seen of Graham's Number, I am going to try and distill her valiant illumination into something digestible—maybe just initially. Before we get anywhere near Graham's Number, we need to gently introduce some new ideas. Here we go!

$2 \uparrow \uparrow 3$. Tetration. Now things get interesting. We have a new word to add to our vocabulary. This time the iterative process is exponentiation. As you might suspect, it is going to create a tower of exponents. Before we get to our example, let's show a simple tower.

$$2^{2^2}$$

The thing with exponent towers is, we always start from the top and make our way down. So now our expression becomes 24, and that equals 16. Okay. That was kind of easy. Umm, that will be the last time we use that word "easy" in talking about tetration, or anything after, for that matter.

$$3^{3^{3^3}}$$

Using parentheses to emphasize the top down order:

$$3^{3^{3^3}} = 3^{3^{(3^3)}} = 3^{3^{27}} = 3^{(3^{27})} = 3^{7,625,597,484,987} = a\ 3.6\ trillion\text{-}digit\ number$$

Yikes! That went off the rails rather quickly. Time to climb bigger mountains. Just adding one more 3 to our tower creates a massive number explosion.

$$3^{3^{3^{3^3}}} = 3^{(3^{3^{3^3}})} = 3^{(3.6\ trillion\text{-}digit\ number)} = \textit{way}\ bigger$$
$$than\ a\ googolplex,\ which\ is\ 10^{(100\text{-}digit\ number)}$$

Before we go any further—yes, further—maybe we should look at what we have been doing to get to this point. That is, we have been doing a hyperoperation sequence. And, to ascribe "levels" to each stage.

Level 0: Counting

1, 2, 3, 4, 5, etc. If we want to go higher, we have to count forward one step at a time. Not very powerful, but it's where we all began, right?

Level 1: Addition

Addition is an iteration up from counting, which we can call "iterated counting"—so instead of doing 3, 4, 5, 6, 7, I can just say 3 + 4 and skip straight to 7. Addition being "iterated counting" means that addition is like a counting *shortcut*—a way to bundle all the counting steps into one, more concise step.

Level 2: Multiplication

One level up, multiplication is iterated addition—an addition shortcut. Instead of saying 2 + 2 + 2 + 2, multiplication allows us to bundle all of those addition steps into one higher-operation step and say 2 × 4. Multiplication is a more powerful operation than addition, and you can create way bigger numbers with it. But we have played a little fast and loose here, because multiplication is not repeated addition. That would fail, for example, when multiplying fractions. So we should be very careful when describing multiplication in terms of addition.

Level 3: Exponentiation ($\uparrow$)

Moving up another level, exponentiation is iterated multiplication. Instead of saying 3 × 3 × 3 × 3, exponentiation allows me to bundle that string into the more concise 34. At this point a new notation, Knuth's arrow ($\uparrow$), can be introduced—3 $\uparrow$ 4. This avoids using the smaller superscript.

Level 4: Tetration (↑ ↑)

Tetration is iterated exponentiation. Before we can understand how to bundle a string of exponentiation the way exponentiation bundles a string of multiplication, we need to understand what a "string of exponentiation" even is. So far, all we've done with exponentiation is one computation—a base number and a power it's raised to. But what if we put two of these computations together, like:

$$2^{2^2}$$

Look at what happens when we add one more step to our tower.

$$3^{3^{3^3}}$$

Using parentheses to emphasize the top-down order:

$$3^{3^{3^3}} = 3^{3^{(3^3)}} = 3^{3^{27}} = 3^{(3^{27})} = 3^{7,625,597,484,987} = \text{a } 3.6 \text{ trillion-digit number}$$

To put things into some valuable perspective, Googol is a hundred-digit number. We created a number that crushes that by merely stacking 3s four high! So where is Graham's Number in all of this? Should we be folding that in about now with this high-octane growth of numbers? Shouldn't this tetration thing be introducing Graham's? The answer to all of those questions is a painful...*no*! We have to continue this hyperoperation sequence two more times! We have to get to Penation, and then finally Hexation. Don't worry. We are going to stop trying to explain the iteration process at this point. It would hurt to even type those definitions in.

Graham's Number: G64

In order to get to G64, we have to start with something called G1, which is hexation. Just to humor ourselves with arrow notation, it would look like this $3 \uparrow \uparrow \uparrow \uparrow 3$. If we unpack the arrow notation and just have a tower of 3s, would you like to guess how many 3s make

up this tower? Actually, a better question—if you are ready for it—
is how high is this tower? How high? You mean like in inches/feet?
The visual is courtesy of waitbutwhy.com. You will also find a more
detailed explanation of what Graham's Number is.

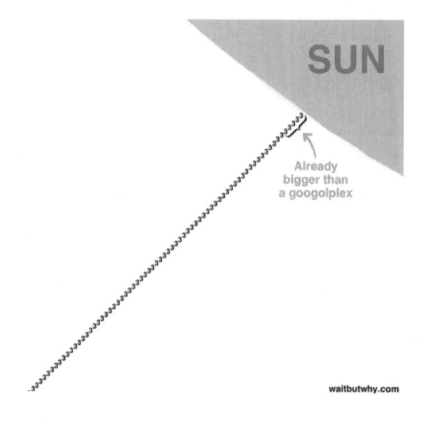

That is not what you were expecting, right? And, as indicated by
the image, as we start coming down this tower, the number quickly
starts blowing by the biggest number that most of the world knows.
This is just G1. G2? It contains a G1 number of arrows. Graham's number is the iteration of iterations! We need to say that again. Graham's
number is the iteration of iterations. Just the number of arrows now
goes beyond the smallest thing to measure the universe in—Planck

lengths. We can't even fathom the number for G2. We have to come to a stop. The whole world actually has to come to a stop, laugh, turn around, and go back home to the sanity of things like exponents. So what is Graham's Number? Let's go back to Evelyn Lamb's title for her *Scientific American* article, "Graham's Number Is Too Big for Me to Tell You How Big It Is." Mind equals blown.

There are more ideas like this about mathematics than can possibly fit in this book—or a thousand books, for that matter. Some are facts, some are problems, and some are extraordinary human feats of creativity. All stretching the domain of mathematics to dimensions that really go beyond any physical measurement, even beyond our collective imaginations. The practicality of mathematics should never be in dispute. If we want our kids to gripped by mathematics, we must give them ideas and concepts that make their eyes pop out and their heads swim. We owe them that, and we owe it to mathematics. [SMP: 1, 2, 4, 7]

Topology

This peculiar field of mathematics is related to geometry but does not resemble the geometry of high school much at all. In topology we are only concerned with the kinds of things that might remain constant even as you allow your mind to bend and stretch them. Take, for instance, the famous Möbius band. Take a long rectangular strip of paper and wrap it into a loop. If you tape both ends together to form a circle, you clearly can see that there is an inside to the loop and an outside. If you take that same strip of paper, and as you wrap it up, you give one end a half-twist, it is impossible to distinguish an inside and an outside of this new loop. You have created a band known as a Möbius band, named after the mathematician to first discuss it in print in the nineteenth century.

Place a pencil in the middle of the strip now and pull the paper under the pencil. If you go long enough, and don't wiggle too much from side to side, your pencil tracing will return to its starting spot. This can be experienced also on the "edge" of the band as well. Place your finger on the fine, sharp edge of the band and trace around the band. You will see something peculiar happens.

These occurrences are accomplished through the simple task of putting one half-twist in the paper band. Try a full-twist, or one and a half twists, and so on, and see what happens. Try cutting along the center line of a Mobius band with a pair of scissors and see what happens.

As a university professor, I (Chris) have had the privilege of teaching a wide variety of courses. One of my favorites has been a course designed for freshmen who enter the university declaring that they are not likely to go much further in mathematics based on their majors. In this course, on the first day of that class, I come well prepared: lots of whiteboard pens, copies of the syllabus, a cup of coffee or glass of water, and a length of rope. The bulk of these items make perfect sense, but the rope tends to get students wondering.

I typically start off with the you're-gonna-love-this-course-because-math-is-so-awesome pep talk and provide them with all the relevant details about assignments and my office hours. When there are roughly fifteen minutes left in the class, I ask two questions related to topology. Holding the glass of water in my open hand, palm up, I present my students with what is sometimes called "The Waiter Problem"—turn this cup around in two circles in the same direction and return it to its original position without spilling a drop. This common trick seems obvious after you have seen it, and I urge you to try it (perhaps with an empty plastic cup first). After this is finished, I pick up the piece of rope and begin to tie one end to my left ankle. While talking incessantly about how mathematics is about watching and observing patterns and behaviors of abstractions or occurrences in nature, I tie the other end to my right ankle, both sides good and tight.

Now comes the question, "Is it possible for me to take off my pants, and put them back on inside out without untying my legs?" After the class stops laughing at the idea of their professor with his pants on the floor, I ask it again. "Is it possible?" Then dismiss the class. "'Bye, see you Wednesday. My office is in WEC 205, if you need to see me before then."

On Wednesday I arrive in class with the rope and a pair of gym shorts under my slacks (phew— you thought I was some kind of exhibitionist, didn't you?). I once again tie my legs together and ask the question, this time to open the class. Invariably there are a few students who actually have tried it back in their dorm rooms, typically without success. Then I perform the trick; loosening my pants, pushing them off my legs, pulling the left leg through the right leg until the pants are right side out but the left ankle hole now faces the left foot and vice versa. The pants are not, however, inside out. To do this, I put them back on but from the bottom of the pants instead of the top, then pull the pants up over my gym shorts, turning them inside out in the process. They end up inside out on my hips.

500
bit.do/MathRecess-Pants-as-Topology

The stretching and twisting of objects as a study has fascinated mathematicians both professional and amateur for hundreds of years. That it isn't taught in school as a real area of disciplined thought is a shame. Some say that topology has its genesis in a classic problem that mathematicians call the Königsberg Bridge problem, which was fully described by Leonhard Euler, an eighteenth-century mathematician who is also known as one of the most prolific mathematical thinkers of all time. The problem is easy to state and grasp but subtle in its solution. We encourage you to go to and see a wonderful description of the problem done by the good people at Numberphile (they produce some of the best mathematics videos on the web). [SMP: 2, 6]

The Seven Bridges of Königsberg, Numberphile
bit.do/mathrecess-Konigsberg

Crazy Things Happen at the Infinity Store
(Chris, so you know who to swear at for the headache)

Here is a simple problem to answer if you want to stay in the finite world. Its solution is often attributed to Carl Gauss. Add the whole numbers from 1 to some other whole number, let's say 100. This might seem a tedious and boring task. But if you were to look at it a little while, you might decide to take a few liberties and you might not go at this from what seems the beginning. Rather, you might move the numbers around a little and try to see some other way around the problem. You might notice, in fact, that if you add the first to the last, you get 101 = 1 + 100, which also happens if you add the second to the next to last 2 + 99 = 101 again, 3 + 98 = ? 4 + 97 etc. till you end up with 50 + 51 all equaling 101. You would deduce that there would be fifty of these 101s, which is easy enough to calculate as 50 (100) + 50(1) or 5050. Simple as that!

But this is not where I want to look; I promised you craziness and infinity. Let's look at a new problem, similar to this one but definitely different. Forever. What is the sum of ALL whole numbers? Stop and think about this a moment, and you will come to the conclusion, I suspect, that the answer is infinity as well. Add an infinite number of numbers, all of them larger than 0, and the sum should grow without bound.

I am here to tell you that this sum fits within this chapter quite well, because it is mind-blowing when you see it. It takes a little bit of patience, so bear with me:

We will need to investigate a few other sums before we can answer the big question, so:

First let's name the sum we want to find S (naming things makes them easier to move around and play with as a single idea), so:

Let's let $S = 1 + 2 + 3 + 4 + 5... + 10,000 + 10,0001 + ...$etc.

Then let's consider another infinite sum:

$S_{with 1s \, and \, -1s} = 1 - 1 + 1 - 1 + 1...$

And then a third one

$S_{with \, negative \, evens} = 1 - 2 + 3 - 4 + 5 - 6...$

To find the mind-blowing result of S, we will look first at $S_{with \, 1s \, and \, -1s}$; you might guess that this sum is 0, which it would be if infinity is an even number, but if it is an odd number then the sum would be 1. What happens then? The simplest answer is to take the average of the two possibilities and say that $S_{with\ 1s\ and\ -1s} = \frac{1}{2}$. (There are other ways to prove that this must be the case, but let's forego them for now and move on to $S_{with\ negative\ evens}$.)

$S_{with\ negative\ evens}$ can be tackled in an ingenious way by first multiplying it by 2, which can be accomplished by adding itself to itself as below, then adding vertically downward...

$$2S_{with\ negative\ evens} = 1 - 2 + 3 - 4 + 5 - 6...$$

$$\underline{ + 1 - 2 + 3 - 4 + 5 - 6...}$$
$$S_{with\ negative\ evens} = 1 - 2 + 3 - 4 + 5 - 6...$$

This says now that is equal to $1S_{with\ 1s\ and\ -1s}$, or in other words, $2S_{with\ negative\ evens} = \frac{1}{2}$, which means that $S_{with\ negative\ evens} = \frac{1}{4}$. And now we are ready for the last little push into crazy town.

Now we will look at the difference between our initial sequence of sums $S = 1 + 2 + 3 + 4...$ and $S_{with\ negative\ evens}$.

$$\underline{S = 1 + 2 + 3 + 4 + 5 + 6 +... - [1 - 2 + 3 - 4 + 5 - 6...]}$$
$$0 + 4 + 0 + 8 + 0 + 12...$$

which is seen more easily as $4 + 8 + 12 + 16 + ...$ This sum has a common factor of 4 in each term. So we can rewrite this whole sum as $4[1 + 2 + 3 + 4 + ...]$ or $4S$.

This leads us to this statement:

$4S = S - S_{with\ negative\ evens}$. Then, if you subtract S from both sides, you get this result: $3S = -S_{with\ negative\ evens}$. Or $3S = - -$ (remember just a few lines up we showed that the sequence with negative evens in it sums up to $\frac{1}{4}$), then when you divide both sides by 3 you get the mind-blowing result of $S = - 1/12$. Please take a moment to think about what this says. If you add up a finite number of whole numbers you get a large number, but if you add up an infinite number of them you get a negative fractional quantity not much different from 0. [SMP: 1, 7, 8]

Even more strange is the fact that this idea plays a role in quantum physics. It is so fundamental a fact that it is stated as a truth, not to be questioned, in most reputable quantum mechanics textbooks, and provides part of the foundation of the mathematics that String Theory is built on. This is a math book, and I am not a physicist, so we won't go any deeper than that except to state it and just revel in the sheer crazy that happens at infinity. Infinity is a good place to "stop" and rest our brains.

It's time to chase a rabbit…

QUESTIONS FOR DEEPER DISCUSSION

1. How can you help your students see math as a tool that can lead them to mind-blowing, even paradoxical truths? How can you move away from presenting math as only a rigid, authoritative set of rules?

2. How can large numbers, crazy sums, and twisted spaces inspire students to think differently and engage productively in their own math experiences?

3. How can you provide your students with opportunities to graze through these fun and mind-blowing mathematic ideas? Consider creating a repository of brain-teasing problems and challenges in a corner of your classroom where students can play when they need a break from standard curricular experiences. Another option is presenting students with a "Problem of the Week."

CHAPTER 8

The Rabbit Hole

*Mathematics is the queen of the sciences and
number theory the queen of mathematics*
—Carl Friedrich Gauss

When Alice went tumbling into the rabbit's hole, her world was turned upside down, and nearly everything she saw was confusing to her. WARNING: Parts of this chapter might have a similar effect on you. Some of what you will encounter will challenge you, and we hope this is the case. We want you to dive in headfirst, and let your mind play with these ideas. Some of these problems and challenges will have explanations that seem obvious right away, and others will require you to ponder awhile. In the spirit of recess, relax, be prepared for a bump or even a bruise, but keep playing. There are plans to create a help community online if you want to join with others in discussing what you find here. We want you to know that these things might not be within your stated curriculum, and we know that, but these topics are tested with children and adults and have been found to provide interest, intrigue, and insightful labor.

We don't spend nearly enough time with arithmetic. Even the simple, practical considerations of strengthening our fluency with basic operations and building capacity for mental math are notable outcomes when students spend time—time considered playful and purposeful—in the deceptively large territory of arithmetic. As we have seen, strength and interest in arithmetic builds the bridge to algebra. Arithmetic builds roads, bridges, tunnels, and countless other structures humans have come to rely on in modern society. In some sense, it is the mathematical equivalent of *Rome*, but with all roads leading *out*.

Arithmetic equals gateway to all.

—James Tanton

Along this journey to the land of variables there is a rabbit hole that lies in wait in the land of arithmetic. This rabbit hole is number theory. Although it has been clearly marked in the history of mathematics, there is little signage for it in math education. It's not even part of most K–12 math curricula. Its study is usually, regrettably, reserved for the university level, which is both sad and ironic because the mathematics is accessible even to first-grade students!

We are all familiar with the rabbit hole being associated with the entrance to the magical world of imagination that awaited Alice. The metaphor of the rabbit hole takes on greater significance when we factor in that Lewis Carroll (Charles Dodgson) used *Alice's Adventures in Wonderland* to offer satirical rebuke to the changing landscape of mathematics—from the sturdy and conservative Euclidean to the wildly imaginative world of imaginary numbers! But is the world of number theory as tantalizingly psychedelic as the world of Alice, The Cheshire Cat, The Caterpillar, and The Mad Hatter? In a nutshell, yes!

We have already met the rabbit—prime numbers! We made sure you chased it early in the book.

> "There are two facts about the distribution of prime numbers. The first is that, [they are] the most arbitrary and ornery objects studied by mathematicians: they grow like weeds among the natural numbers, seeming to obey no other law than that of chance, and nobody can predict where the next one will sprout. The second fact is even more astonishing, for it states just the opposite: that the prime numbers exhibit stunning regularity, that there are laws governing their behavior, and that they obey these laws with almost military precision."
>
> Don Zager

$$2 \quad 3 \quad 5 \quad 7 \quad 11 \quad 13 \quad 17 \quad 19 \quad 23 \quad 29 \quad 31 \quad 37 \quad 41 \quad 43 \quad 47\cdots$$

Before we fall deliriously into this hole that Gauss called the *Queen of Mathematics*, we should not overlook the actual act of falling down the rabbit hole. Or rather, perhaps we should entertain the idea that this stumbling is a beautiful acknowledgement of the uniqueness of each of us and the imaginative portraits that wait to be drawn by each and every one of our students.

There are no rules, constraints, or limits inside the rabbit hole. This tour, which offers only a glimpse, will be a carefree skip and romp through some of the most alluring fields of mathematics. Ready? Just follow prime numbers…the *rabbit*!

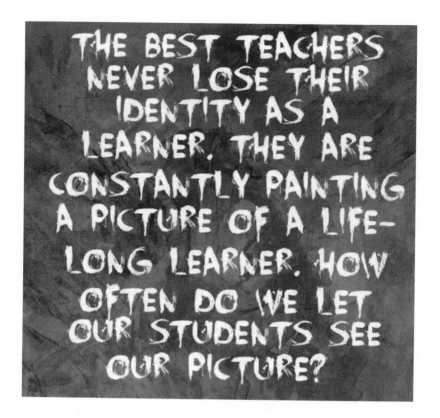

THE BEST TEACHERS NEVER LOSE THEIR IDENTITY AS A LEARNER. THEY ARE CONSTANTLY PAINTING A PICTURE OF A LIFE-LONG LEARNER. HOW OFTEN DO WE LET OUR STUDENTS SEE OUR PICTURE?

Primes

It is perhaps fated that the foundational aspect of all numbers has been entangled in the world's most famous unsolved problem—the Riemann Hypothesis. There really isn't a simple explanation of what that is. The crudest idea would be that it has to do with how prime numbers are distributed, but it is literally far, far more complex than that! It's like Alice going through The Looking Glass and entering the fantastical world of imaginary numbers. The truth of the behavior of primes lies somewhere in that still mysterious mathematical *goo*. To be frank, you would need a solid background in university mathematics to understand the problem, never mind take a stab at making sense of all these orderly weeds.

I have to thank my own kids for reinvigorating my fascination with prime numbers. Before I started playing Prime Climb with them, my knowledge of which numbers are prime didn't really venture confidently outside of 100. The last number on the Prime Climb board is 101. Although the game ends there, the collective curiosities of my children didn't. When my daughter asked what the next prime number was, I hesitantly offered up 103. Her question—children posing questions shows a desire to organically *own* mathematics—is what spurred knowing all the primes in the next block of a hundred numbers.

Here is a specific sequence of prime numbers: 89, 97, 101, 103, 107, 109, 113.

Why is this significant? Look at the gaps between the primes, 8, 4, 2, 4, 2, 4. The widest gap of primes in the first one hundred numbers is eight. It then oscillates for a brief moment between four and two. What do you think the next prime number is after 113? Keep in mind that prime numbers have this *mathematical arrhythmia*, demonstrating no pattern between them.

The next prime number is 127. The gap widens to fourteen. I found this astonishing and almost counterintuitive. Numbers like 117, 119, or 123—surely one of them *had to be* prime! Why couldn't I anchor myself to these numbers being composites? That's because our math facts of recalling times tables is contained within a 12×12 grid. We never intersected 39×3 (117), 17×7 (119), or 41×3 (123). I shouldn't have waited forty years to continue learning multiplication facts. Then again, a game like Prime Climb wasn't around. Neither were my kids! There is something wonderfully hypnotic about the gaps between primes—a roller coaster of even numbers. Below are the gaps of all the primes between the numbers 2 and 200:

1, 2, 2, 4, 2, 4, 2, 4, 6, 2, 6, 4, 2, 4, 6, 6, 2, 6, 4, 2, 6, 4, 6, 8,
4, 2, 4, 2, 4, 14, 4, 6, 2, 10, 2, 6, 6, 4, 6, 6, 2, 10, 2, 4, 2, 12,
12, 4, 2, 4, 6, 2, 10, 6, 6, 6, 2, 6, 4, 2

Sieve of Eratosthenes

The Sieve of Eratosthenes is not only a nice way for students to see prime numbers pop out, but it creates a nice historical linkage to a famous mathematician who is often called the Father of Geography (he was the first to measure the circumference of the earth). What is nice about the Sieve is that students are constantly reminded of the definitions of prime numbers and composite numbers. In the short video below, there is a whimsical look at how to find the primes using the Sieve. Having a mere definition of prime numbers is not enough. The physical construction activity from Chapter 2 and Eratosthenes' clever technique of filtering out the *mathematical atoms* are critical foundational pieces for elementary students. [SMP: 1, 6, 7]

Below is a link to a visual explanation by the energetic Eddie Woo (@misterwootube).

The Sieve of Eratosthenes
bit.do/mathrecess-eratosthenes

Prime Factorization

One of the most tragic elements—I don't use that word lightly—is that this important mathematical technique is introduced far too late in math education. It shouldn't have to be a middle-school topic. That is why it was introduced early in this book! As soon as students are getting comfortable with multiplying, prime factorization needs to be rolled out.

Take, for example, when kids learn about numbers that multiply to 24. The one that always seems to be left out is 8 × 3. I doubt that would be the case if students broke down 24 into its prime factors of 2 × 2 × 2 × 3. Now ask kids to choose to multiply any of these factors so that the result leave only two numbers multiplied by each other. This is what should result:

    (2 × 2) × (2 × 3) = 4 × 6
    (2) × (2 × 2 × 3) = 2 × 12
    (2 × 2 × 2) × (3) = 8 × 3

The next number you want to try could be anything, but I might recommend 60, for the simple reason it has lots of factors and has historical linkages to the Babylonians using it as a base. This might be a good time to ask students why they chose this number as a base. It could turn into a great discussion about bases! Pinterest is a great resource for powerful visual creations. Here is a nice one that would be good to make a poster:

PRIME NUMBERS LIST

2	3	5	7	11	13	17	19	23	29
31	37	41	43	47	53	59	61	67	71
73	79	83	89	97	101	103	107	109	113
127	131	137	139	149	151	157	163	167	173
179	181	191	193	197	199	211	223	227	229

FACTORS LIST

1: 1
2: (1, 2)
3: (1, 3)
4: (1, 2, 4)
5: (1, 5)
6: (1, 2, 3, 6)
7: (1, 7)
8: (1, 2, 4, 8)
9: (1, 3, 9)
10: (1, 2, 5, 10)
11: (1, 11)
12: (1, 2, 3, 4, 6, 12)
13: (1, 13)
14: (1, 2, 7, 14)
15: (1, 3, 5, 15)
16: (1, 2, 4, 8, 16)
17: (1, 17)
18: (1, 2, 3, 6, 9, 18)
19: (1, 19)
20: (1, 2, 4, 5, 10, 20)
21: (1, 3, 7, 21)
22: (1, 2, 11, 22)
23: (1, 23)
24: (1, 2, 3, 4, 6, 8, 12, 24)
25: (1, 5, 25)
26: (1, 2, 13, 26)
27: (1, 3, 9, 27)
28: (1, 2, 4, 7, 14, 28)
29: (1, 29)
30: (1, 2, 3, 5, 6, 10, 15, 30)
31: (1, 31)
32: (1, 2, 4, 8, 16, 32)
33: (1, 3, 11, 33)
34: (1, 2, 17, 34)
35: (1, 3, 7, 35)
36: (1, 2, 3, 4, 6, 9, 12, 18, 36)
37: (1, 37)
38: (1, 2, 19, 38)
39: (1, 3, 13, 39)
40: (1, 2, 4, 5, 8, 10, 20, 40)
41: (1, 41)
42: (1, 2, 3, 6, 7, 14, 21, 42)
43: (1, 43)
44: (1, 2, 4, 11, 22, 44)
45: (1, 3, 5, 9, 15, 45)
46: (1, 2, 23, 46)
47: (1, 47)
48: (1, 2, 3, 4, 6, 8, 12, 16, 24, 48)
49: (1, 7, 49)
50: (1, 2, 5, 10, 25, 50)
51: (1, 3, 17, 51)
52: (1, 2, 4, 13, 26, 52)
53: (1, 53)
54: (1, 2, 3, 6, 9, 18, 27, 54)
55: (1, 5, 11, 55)
56: (1, 2, 4, 7, 8, 14, 28, 56)
57: (1, 3, 19, 57)
58: (1, 2, 29, 58)
59: (1, 59)
60: (1, 2, 3, 4, 5, 6, 10, 12, 15, 20, 30, 60)
61: (1, 61)
62: (1, 2, 31, 82)
63: (1, 3, 7, 9, 21, 63)
64: (1, 2, 4, 8, 16, 32, 64)
65: (1, 5, 13, 65)
66: (1, 2, 3, 6, 11, 22, 33, 66)
67: (1, 67)
68: (1, 2, 4, 17, 34, 68)
69: (1, 3, 23, 69)
70: (1, 2, 5, 7, 10, 14, 35, 70)
71: (1, 71)
72: (1, 2, 3, 4, 6, 8, 9, 12, 18, 24, 36, 72)
73: (1, 73)
74: (1, 2, 37, 74)
75: (1, 3, 5, 15, 25, 75)
76: (1, 2, 4, 19, 38, 76)
77: (1, 7, 11, 77)
78: (1, 2, 3, 6, 13, 26, 39, 78)
79: (1, 79)
80: (1, 2, 4, 5, 8, 10, 16, 20, 40, 80)
81: (1, 3, 9, 27, 81)
82: (1, 2, 41, 82)
83: (1, 83)
84: (1, 2, 3, 4, 6, 7, 12, 14, 21, 28, 42, 84)
85: (1, 5, 17, 85)
86: (1, 2, 43, 86)
87: (1, 3, 29, 87)
88: (1, 2, 4, 8, 11, 22, 44, 88)
89: (1, 89)
90: (1, 2, 3, 5, 6, 9, 10, 15, 18, 30, 45, 90)
91: (1, 7, 13, 91)
92: (1, 2, 4, 23, 46, 92)
93: (1, 3, 31, 93)
94: (1, 2, 47, 94)
95: (1, 5, 19, 95)
96: (1, 2, 3, 4, 6, 8, 12, 16, 24, 32, 48, 96)
97: (1, 97)
98: (1, 2, 7, 14, 49, 98)
99: (1, 3, 9, 11, 33, 99)
100: (1, 2, 4, 5, 10, 20, 25, 50, 100)

List of Factors: Numbers 1 to 100

There is another idea to tack on here which really doesn't get explored until high school! If we agree that prime factorization is a beneficial and vibrant activity to do with elementary students, then maybe we should show kids a compact way of showing something like 2 × 2 × 2—with *exponents!* In the beginning kids will forget the new notation of 2^3 and multiply the two numbers, but so what? We all forget new stuff—at any age! The idea of sharing exponents at any early age is completely within their wheelhouse of understanding and interest. They will feel especially proud when they can write a number like $40 = 2^3 \times 5$ and correctly voice their newfangled expression! This knowledge will aid in solving some factor-type questions in really cool ways. [SMP: 1, 7, 8]

Sum of Factors

Let's start with a question we can do by simply listing all the factors and adding them up. What is the sum of the factors of 20? The factors are 1, 2, 4, 5, 10, and 20. If you add them up, you get 42. Pretty straightforward, right? There is another way, which, not too surprisingly, opens up a middle-school topic much earlier on—the distribution property of multiplication. For some reason, distribution becomes mangled with that acronym FOIL (first-outer-inner-last) and polynomials, and all intuition flies out the window. Don't let students be a passenger here. Let them take the wheel and get an honest feel for this critical math property. Let's examine the following question:

$(1 + 2)(3 + 4)$

After easily dealing with the parentheses, the question simply becomes what is 3×7? At this point, knowing the answer right away is not critical, and bringing your students to a collective pause could be a good thing. Not knowing a math fact is a good thing? In the rabbit hole it is! Now impose this restriction on the students—you cannot do the addition in the parentheses first! *What? No way!* Yeah, that will be the response of many of your students. Let them wallow in that uncomfortable state for a bit. Tell them to start multiplying. Pretty sure they will give you a vacant look that says, *Multiply what?* Remember the endgame here—we want students to *own the idea of distribution.* We simply do not want to announce it like we do with so much of mathematics. Ask kids to pick one number from one bracket and multiply it with another number from the other bracket. Doesn't matter which one.

$$(1 + 2)(3 + 4) = 2 \times 3...$$

However long it takes, ask students to determine what they should do next. If students pick a different pair, they are on their way to taking possession of the distributive property of multiplication. The end result will, of course, look something like this:

$$(1 + 2)(3 + 4) = (2 \times 3) + (1 \times 3) + (1 \times 4) + (2 \times 4)$$
$$= 6 + 3 + 4 + 8$$
$$= 21$$

Forget FOIL. Having students experience a real mathematical epiphany will negate the need to go through the mnemonic minefield of FOIL, SOHCAHTOA, and CAST. A valuable follow-up question here would be to ask your students how many times they have to multiply when there are two numbers in each bracket? How about two in one, and three in the other? In just another two-minute conversation, elementary students should understand the number of "terms" will be the product of the number of terms in each bracket. Every number needs to dance with every number in another bracket. End it on a whimsical note!

Getting back to the sum of the factors of 20. The prime factorization of 20 results in $2^2 \times 5$, but to aid in the understanding of exponents, write it like $2^2 \times 5^1$. One last thing. A big thing. Because 1 is a factor of 20, we need a way to show that with exponents, so we use the exponent 0. There is more sophistication here than this explanation, but if you can get your students to temporarily buy that, then what they, *and you,* are about to discover is pretty sweet.

Any number that is a factor you write out with exponents, always starting from 0 to the largest exponent. In this example, it will become:

$$(2^0 + 2^1 + 2^2)(5^0 + 5^1)$$
$$= (1 + 2 + 4)(1 + 5)$$

Using PEMDAS (parenthesis, exponents, multiplication, division, addition, subtraction) quickly gives you 42, the answer to our original question; HOWEVER, if students take the care to multiply first and get six terms, they will find all the factors of 20. Now you see why we spent time with students learning distribution! Pretty cool, huh? [SMP: 1, 7, 8]

Locker Problem

One hundred students are assigned lockers one through one hundred. The student assigned to locker number one opens all one hundred lockers. The student assigned to locker number two then closes all lockers whose numbers are multiples of 2. The student assigned to locker number three changes the status of all lockers whose numbers are multiples of 3 (e.g., locker number three, which is open, gets closed, and locker number six, which is closed, gets opened). The student assigned to locker number four changes the status of all lockers whose numbers are multiples of 4, and so on for all one hundred lockers.

This is a classic math problem usually introduced in middle school, but with some background given in this chapter, the question can be tackled by students in the upper part of elementary school. A way to ensure this happens is to zero in on an already used problem-solving technique—start with a simpler problem. How about ten lockers? Here is what the lockers will look like in terms of "openness."

Locker 1 Student:	1	2	3	4	5	6	7	8	9	10
Locker 2 Student:	1		3		5		7		9	
Locker 3 Student:	1					6				
Locker 4 Student:	1			4				8		
Locker 5 Student:	1			4						10
Locker 6 Student:	1									
Locker 7 Student:	1									
Locker 8 Student:	1									
Locker 9 Student:	1									
Locker 10 Student:	1									

Hmmm. Only lockers one and four remain open if there are ten students and ten lockers. Why these numbers? Anything special about them? Hard to tell at this point. Here are the questions to give students—with answers.

1. Which lockers will be left open? *1, 4, 9, 16, 25, 36, 49, 64, 81, 100*
2. What do you notice about these particular locker numbers? *Perfect squares*
3. Why were these lockers left unopened? *Odd number of factors*
4. How many lockers, and which ones, were touched exactly twice? *Twenty-five.*

   2, 3, 5, 7, 11, 13, 17, 19, 23, 29, 31, 37, 41, 43, 47, 53, 59, 61, 67, 71, 73, 79,83, 89, 97; they are the prime numbers, which only have two factors.

Note that the order in which the students discover which lockers are in which state might not follow the order of these questions. Some students will see very quickly that the result is dependent on whether a locker is touched an even or an odd number of times (hence the odd number of factors answer to question three above). It's important to not be too anxious to get to the answer. The play is part of the learning. [SMP: 1, 2, 3, 4, 7, 8]

The Characters (Some) of Number Theory!

The story of Alice in Wonderland and the rabbit hole is a nice metaphor for number theory. It is serving our purpose well for giving a trippy foray into one of the most gripping branches of mathematics, but it is much bigger and denser in this chapter. Perhaps some of your students will carry on in this trek later in life. We hope they do!

What we should do now is introduce some of the whimsical "characters" that constitute this vast land. It is hardly a complete list, but it's a nice snapshot.

Abundant Numbers

A number is abundant if the sum of its proper divisors (aliquot parts) is greater than the number. Twelve is the first abundant number, because the sum of its divisors—1, 2, 3, 4, and 6—have a sum greater than 12. Can you find several more? Are there any patterns to these? [SMP: 1, 3, 7, 8]

Amicable Numbers

Amicable numbers are pairs of numbers, each of which is the sum of the other's aliquot divisors. For example, 220 and 284 are amicable numbers, whereas all the aliquot divisors of 220, i.e., 110, 55, 44, 22, 10, 5, 4, 2, and 1, add up to 284, and all the aliquot divisors of 284, i.e., 142, 71, 4, 2, and 1, add up to 220. Interestingly enough, there are a great many pairs of amicable numbers, and they remain a topic of investigation to hobby mathematicians with computers. This pair, 220 and 284, were, along with the next smallest pair (two numbers less than 2,000) were known to the Greeks. Two other sets were found by some unknown mathematicians from the Arabian Peninsula before the eighteenth century. Then came Leonhard Euler, who always comes up in stories of mathematics because he was so prolific. He found thirty more pairs on his own. It is an interesting research challenge for older students to look up his method for finding them. [SMP: 1, 2, and 3]

Circular Primes

A circular prime number is one that remains a prime number after repeatedly relocating the first digit of the number to the end of the number. For example, 197, 971, and 719 are all prime numbers. Similarly, 1193, 1931, 9311, and 3119 are all prime numbers. Other numbers that satisfy the definition are 11, 13, 37, 79, 113, 199, and 337. Can you find the next two? [SMP: 1, 8]

Cyclic Numbers

A cyclic number is a number of "n" digits that when multiplied by 1, 2, 3, ... n, results in the same digits but in a different order. For example, the number 142,857 is a cyclic number because 142,857 × 2 = 285,714, 142,857 × 3 = 428,571, 142,857 × 4 = 571,428, and so on. It is not known just how many cyclic numbers exist. If you look at 142,857 though, you might notice that this is closely related to the decimal expansion of ⅐, which is a repeating decimal. This has led to the conjecture that there are an infinite number of cyclic numbers, but so far this remains unproven. One item of note, though, is that these cyclic numbers are related to and generated by a certain subset of the prime numbers, like 7 or 17. These primes all generate the longest possible sequences of digits in their decimal expansions. [SMP: 1 (Most definitely, there are people still actively working on establishing this as a fact; come join in the fun.)]

Deficient Numbers

Deficient numbers are part of the family of numbers that are either deficient, perfect, or abundant.

Digital Root

The digital root (DR) of a number is the single digit that results from the continuous summation of the digits of the number and the numbers resulting from each summation. For example, consider the number 7,935. The summation of its digits is 24. The summation of 2 and 4 is 6, the digital root of 7,935. Digital roots are used to check addition and multiplication by means of a method called casting out 9s. For example, check the summation of 378 and 942. The DR of 378 is 9, 3 + 7 + 8 = 18, 1 + 8 = 9. The DR of 942 is 6, 9 + 4 + 2 = 15, 1 + 5 = 6. Adding 9 and 6 produces 15. The DR of 15 is 6, 1 + 5 = 6. The summation of 378 and 942 is 1,320. The DR of 1,320 is 6. With the two final DRs equal, the addition is correct.

Happy Numbers

Happy numbers are those numbers for which, after successively adding the squares of the digits of the number, the end result is the number 1. The number 23 is a happy number. Square each of its digits and add, i.e., $2^2 + 3^2 = 13$; then $1^2 + 3^2 = 10$; then $1^2 + 0^2 = 1$. Because the final number is a 1, the number 23 is a happy number. There are only seventeen two-digit happy numbers—10, 13, 19, 23, 28, 31, 32, and so on. Can you find some more?

Narcissistic Numbers

Narcissistic numbers are those "n" digit numbers that can be derived from the sum of the "nth" powers of the digits of the number. For example, if $N = 100A + 10B + C = A^3 + B^3 + C^3$, the number N is narcissistic. The most basic example of this is the $153 = 1^3 + 5^3 + 3^3$. Three other well-known examples are 370, 371, and 407. Can you find any others? [SMP: 2, 7]

Sad Numbers

As you guessed it, these are numbers that are not happy! And this is just a small sampling of the richness that numbers demonstrate. Sometimes straightforward. Sometimes quirky. Sometimes cheeky.

Modular Arithmetic

Modular/Clock Arithmetic

Modulus 12

One of the sad ironies that occurs in school is that when students stare at a clock in class out of boredom, they are staring at modular arithmetic—and they are indirectly and unconsciously learning its basic idea. That is the idea of "wrapping around," reaching a certain value, and then cycling through those numbers again and again and again....

In the twelve-hour clock, the day is divided into two twelve-hour periods. If the time is 7:00 now, then eight hours later it will be 3:00. Usual addition would suggest that the later time should be 7 + 8 = 15, but this is not the answer because clock time "wraps around" every twelve hours. Because the hour number starts over after it reaches 12, this is arithmetic *modulo* twelve. Let's say (starting at 12) you want to know what the time will be in thirty-eight hours. The question, using notation of modular arithmetic, looks like this: 38 = ?(mod 12). Do you see what this is really asking? It's asking for the *remainder*! The answer to this question is 2. It is now 2 pm or 2 am, depending on what time you started with.

As we are wrapping around the clock, we will pass 2 more than once. We can talk about *congruence* here. After fourteen hours or thirty-eight hours, the clock will be showing 2 o'clock.

$$38 \equiv 14 \ (\text{mod } 12)$$

Of course, we can create any kind of clock—modulus—that we want. The number in front of the bracket, if there is no congruence, denotes the wrap-around remainder. Kids have already seen a clock and done some basic division. Now they can speak in modular arithmetic.

$27 \equiv 2$ (mod 5) 27 divided by 5 has a remainder of 2
$29 \equiv 14$ (mod 5) 29 is congruent to 14 in modulus 5

We are not going to go to much further here, because modular arithmetic has its own rabbit hole into some very deep ideas about the relationship of numbers. It can help you if you want to investigate more deeply those Cyclic Numbers we talked about earlier. The UPC bar labels and ISBN codes you see on all products and books all make use of modular arithmetic to ensure the validity of the code when it is read by a machine. One of the most important applications of modular arithmetic is in cryptography, with encrypting web traffic and financial transactions as examples.

A fun way to play with modular arithmetic is to take it out of its mathematical context and apply it in context with everyday words. Here the word modulo means "ignore." So, for example,

> a and A are identical modulo capitalization, or iPad is identical to iTouch modulo size. See what kind of examples your students might come up with, having fun with definition!

Chinese Remainder Theorem

Around the third century, the Chinese mathematician Sunzi posed this question:

There are certain things whose number is unknown. If we count them by threes, we have two left over; by fives, we have three left over; and by sevens, two are left over. How many things are there?

Now that we have some modular arithmetic under our belts, we can express this question in compact notation.

$$? = 2(\text{mod } 3)? = 3(\text{mod } 5)? = 2(\text{mod } 7)$$

Because the answer is a relatively easy number to work with—23—a good investigation would be to give kids blocks (<30) and see whether they can work out this question by dividing blocks into piles and see what number of blocks yields all three clues and conditions.

Divisibility Rules

Nothing strengthens the fluency of math facts like knowing the basic rules of divisibility from the numbers 1 to 12. I (Sunil) went through all the rules with both my kids by the time they were ten. Some are well known and intuitive, and others require a little more elaboration and deeper dive as to their rules. They are the colorful addition to the palette of number sense and number theory. It should be noted that all of these rules apply so long as we are working strictly within the confines of our base ten, place-value system of expressing quantities. Chris is fond of making graduate students demonstrate that the divisibility rule stated here for 3 is not true in base 3.

1. Any integer is divisible by 1.
2. Any integer ending in 0, 2, 4, 6, or 8 is divisible by 2.
3. Add up all the digits. If the sum is divisible by 3, so is the number: 381 = 3 + 8 + 1 = 12. This is divisible by 3 (Note: you can repeat this.)
4. If the last two digits are divisible by 4, then the entire number is divisible by 4. Why?
5. If the last digit ends in a 0 and a 5, then the number is divisible by 5.
6. If the last digit is even and divisible by 3 (Rules 2 and 3), then the number is divisible by 6.
7. Double the last digit and then subtract it from the remaining digits. If this number is divisible by 7, then the number is divisible by 7—such as 672. Double 2 to get 4. Subtract 4 from 67, and you get 63.
8. If the last three digits are divisible by 8, then the number is divisible by 8. If you can halve the number at least three times, then it also shows divisibility by 8.
9. If the sum of the digits is divisible by 9 (similar to the rule of 3), then the whole number is divisible by 9.
10. If the number ends in a 0, then it is divisible by 10.

11. Add and subtract the digits in alternating order. If the result is divisible by 11, so is the number. For example, 3729. 3-7 + 2-9 =-11. This is divisible by 11.

12. If number is divisible by both 3 and 4, then it will be divisible by 12.

Odds/Evens (Courtesy of Peter Harrison)

Whole numbers can be divided into even and odd numbers. Any whole number that can be divided exactly (with no remainder) by 2 is called an even number. Zero is considered to be an even number. If a whole number cannot be divided exactly by 2, then it is called an odd number.

Here are some great questions to answer in terms of ODD or EVEN!

- The sum of two even numbers
- The sum of three odd numbers
- The sum of two even and one odd number
- The sum of an even number of odd numbers
- The sum of an odd number of even numbers
- The sum of an odd number of odd numbers
- The difference between two odd numbers
- The difference between two even numbers
- The difference between an odd and an even number
- The product of two even numbers
- The product of two odd numbers
- The product of an even and an odd number
- An even number multiplied by itself
- An even number raised to an odd exponent
- An odd number raised to an even exponent

- An even number added to 1
- An odd number added to 1
- An odd number added to 2
- An even number added to 2
- The sum of three consecutive numbers starting with an odd number
- The sum of three consecutive numbers starting with an even number

[SMP: 1, 2, 3, and 7]

medium.com/@sunilsingh_42118/
the-rabbit-hole-of-mathematics-4930d3bdce39

The Golden Ratio

If you are a fan of the Dan Brown novels about an academic with a penchant for tracking down ancient conspiracies, then you are likely familiar with his popular book *The DaVinci Code*. In this book, Brown paints some deep, dark, mystical pictures about the Fibonacci Sequence, which begins at 1 and is followed by another 1, and then each subsequent member of the sequence is found through adding the immediately previous two members.

1
1
1 + 1 = 2
2 + 1 = 3
3 + 2 = 5
5 + 3 = 8
13
21
34

55

89

Brown's protagonist, Robert Langdon, finds this sequence in all sorts of art, architecture, plants, and patterns in religious sacraments. This use of numbers is titillating and exciting but misses the best parts.

This sequence is linked to the golden ratio, which, from the standpoint of Number Theory, is even more interesting than is the ubiquitous Pi. Both Pi and Phi (the name given to the golden ratio) are among that amazing set of numbers called irrational. A case can be made that Phi is the most irrational of all irrational numbers. This case is not hard to make or follow, but it does require some deep background.

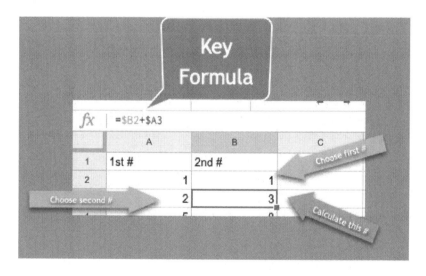

Using any spreadsheet, you can generate these values easily.

1

Prior or Given #	Calculated #
1	1
2	3
5	8
13	21
34	55
89	144
233	377
610	987
1597	2584
4181	6765
10946	17711
28657	46368
75025	121393

Repeat the calculations, always adding the last two numbers together. This may be fun practice for adding but to get a lot done in a hurry, automate it with a spreadsheet program. Notice that these numbers grow large, but not in a particularly rapid rate.

Prior or Given #	Calculated #		Ratios
1	1		1
2	3		1.5
5	8		1.6
13	21		1.615384615
34	55		1.617647059
89	144		1.617977528
233	377		1.618025751
610	987		1.618032787
1597	2584		1.618033813
4181	6765		1.618033963
10946	17711		1.618033985
28657	46368		1.618033988
75025	121393		1.618033989
196418	317811		1.618033989
514229	832040		1.618033989
1346269	2178309		1.618033989
3524578	5702887		1.618033989
9227465	14930352		1.618033989
24157817	39088169		1.618033989
63245986	102334155		1.618033989
165580141	267914296		1.618033989
433494437	701408733		1.618033989

Notice this column ends up looking the same...

Notice that the numbers in the ratios column settle on a single value, that of 1.618033989. We cannot see the remaining digits. You can guess that they are not the same, just because you know that the numbers used to create these ratios (the values in columns B and A) are different from row to row. Somewhere to the right in these decimals, the values in column D row "X" are different from those in column D row "X+1".

In fact, these missing values way off to the right can be shown to wander around for long periods of time between "settling down" at any one value for a location. This tendency is what makes Phi a most irrational quantity, not only cannot it *not* be fully expressed as a ratio between two numbers, but fractions that approximate it have to grow the number of their digits extremely large before you can see, for instance, the fortieth decimal place get fixed. This is a highly irrational number. Of course, in the modern classroom we can do these explorations now, we have spreadsheets, and Wolfram Alpha to aid our long, distant calculations for us, and all we need do is check closely what is happening. [SMP: 1, 4, 5, 6]

For a wonderfully clear and animated description of what was just discussed, watch this video by the people at Numberphile.

The Golden Ratio (why it is so irrational), Numberphile
bit.do/mathrecess-Phi

Numbers, you see, are the fodder for so many flights of fancy. Charles Dodson (better known as Lewis Carroll, author of the *Alice* books) was a mathematician, teacher, and logician. He even has a mathematical method named after him. It is used for working with arrays of numbers. (That's not part of this book, just backstory.) Dodson wrote *Alice's Adventures in Wonderland* for his niece to entertain her but also to send her down rabbit holes where logic had to be employed. He thought that placing challenging ideas before her would encourage her to engage her mind but in a playful manner. This has been our hope as well in this chapter.

QUESTIONS FOR DEEPER DISCUSSION

1. The prime numbers are everywhere in the curriculum, typically in uninteresting or strictly utilitarian settings. They present a great many interesting problems, though. How can you place one or two of these ideas in front of your students to work with?

2. How has your perception of the numbers we use every day changed in reading this book so far?

3. Choose one of the ideas above that seemed new or interesting to you and take the time to look into it more deeply. How could you present this idea to your students in a fun and engaging way?

CHAPTER 9

Pure Imagination

The visionary starts with a clean sheet
of paper and reimagines the world.
—Malcolm Gladwell

Aging can certainly make us wiser, but that wisdom, generally speaking, tends to recede from the innocent and boundless ideas of being a child. We distance ourselves from those ideas that seem foolish, ridiculous, impractical, unrealistic, and generally incompatible in the adult world of order and compliance. That means we drift further away from things like risk-taking and dreaming. Imagination becomes barely a speck in our rearview mirror—if we care to look at all.

Now it's time to look—backwards, forwards, sideways, and *slantways* at the complete reconstruction of math education. We must have the courage and curiosity to contemplate Gladwell's blank sheet of paper. If we are going to debate and argue like weathered and jaded adults about the cost and practicality of starting from zero, then that is all the more reason to contemplate disrupting our most traditional concepts of learning mathematics.

In a scene from movie *Willy Wonka and The Chocolate Factory*, the remaining characters are licking wallpaper made of fruit. When Wonka remarks that the snozzberries taste like snozzberries, the spoiled and smug Veruca Salt offers, "Who has ever heard of a snozz-berry?" Wonka replies with a classic opening line from Arthur O'Shaughnessy's *Ode*, "We are the music makers, and we are the dreamers of dreams." Here is the entire first verse:

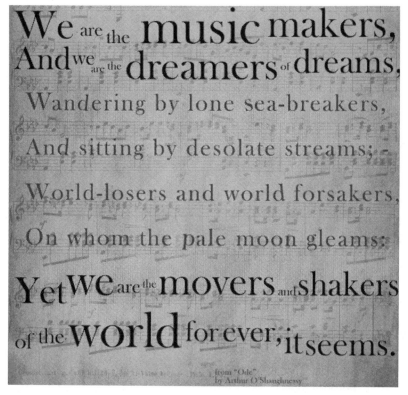

We are the music makers,
And we are the dreamers of dreams,
Wandering by lone sea-breakers,
And sitting by desolate streams;—
World-losers and world forsakers,
On whom the pale moon gleams:
Yet we are the movers and shakers
of the world for ever, it seems.

from "Ode"
by Arthur O'Shaughnessy

In many ways, we feel like we're forever imagining a mathematical word filled with snozzberries that require quirky paths to uncover their delight. As David Farragut said in 1864 aboard the USS *Hartford*, "Damn the torpedoes, full speed ahead."

Here we go. Dream big or go home.

QED: Questioning Every Dogma

In 2017—thanks to the alchemic powers of social media—Junaid Mubeen and I (Sunil) launched *QED*, a *Medium* blog devoted solely to math articles pushing the anachronistic boundaries in math education.

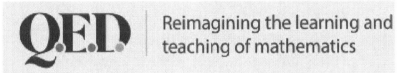

Junaid's academic background—a doctorate in mathematics from Oxford University and a master's from Harvard University—is dwarfed only by his humility and passion in communicating mathematics to the world. Soon after starting *QED*, we added another integral spirit to our team, Matthew Beyranevand. Matthew and I have the same birthday, May 27. That isn't a coincidence. We are identical in our thoughts on reimagining the learning and teaching of mathematics.

QED now has more than three thousand followers. The community members are encouraged to submit to us their deepest and dearest ideas of math education. Disruption? We eat that for breakfast at *QED*.

Below are some of the titles from the roughly one hundred articles sitting in the *QED* incubation chamber:

- "A Mathematician Is Like a Naturalist"
- "You Weren't Bad at Math, You Just Weren't Looking at It the Right Way"
- "Math for Pleasure, Math for a New Generation"
- "There Exists an Elegant, Lovely, and Inspiring School for Mathematics"

- "The Unreasonableness of K–12 Mathematics"
- "It Is Time to Throw Away the Dickensian Culture of Math Education"

The contributions have come from all over the world. There is an energy of change rippling through math education. It's time to build. Deeply, fearlessly, and quickly.

Imagination Requires Strong Foundation

One of the many myths floating around math education is that anything that is inquiry-based is somehow going to be all fuzzy and weak on facts. One could only imagine what a traditionalist might think if there were this metaphorical idea of skipping along with Willy Wonka in creating a brand-new curriculum. If we are going to get our students into the deep end of the mathematical pool, they need to know how to tread water with solid understanding of not only math facts but the interplay between them. Something like Graham's Number will not be nearly as captivating if there is no understanding of multiplication and exponentiation.

Even the wildest ideas of how students and teachers could explore mathematics must have woven the trio of fluencies—factual, procedural, and conceptual. If the concept of three fluencies seems unfamiliar, Chris recorded a podcast with Cathy Carroll, a researcher at the highly respected West Ed, on this very topic, and you can listen to it here:

Episode 29, Mathematical Fluency: What does it Mean, Why is it Important? AIMS Center Blog
bit.do/mathrecess-zpc29

I came across this question and this 20-year-old British game show via one of Junaid Mubeen's 2016 presentations, "Everyone in Your School Could Be a Maths Genius."

"Everyone in Your School Could Be a Maths Genius," Dr. Junaid Mubeen
bit.do/mathrecess10

For those not familiar with the show *Countdown*, contestants have to use all six numbers with basic operations to create a question that answers the target number—and in thirty seconds! What is remarkable about the solution is that it didn't actually involve needing to know a certain large multiplication computation, which was, paradoxically, critical to the solution. To speed things up, let's go halfway into the solution:

$(100 + 6) \times 3$

We are sitting comfortably at 318. Hmmm. To get to our target number, it seems we could multiply by 3 and then subtract 2 to reach our number of 952. The problem is you can only use each of the given numbers once. What do you do with 75, 50, and 25? The little bit of mathematical sorcery employed by James Martin, the wily contestant on the show, can be seen in the video. Even better, perhaps you and your students can muster out the solution! [SMP: 1, 2, 3, 7]

Principles for Problem-Solving

Problem-solving has been a call to action for the National Council of Teachers of Mathematics (NCTM) for almost forty years. It requires ownership of understanding to truly know why and how things are related and working in mathematics. Good problem-solving develops all the key benchmarks of mathematical thinking, which include, but are not limited to, curiosity, resilience, and persistence.

Perhaps it is a good idea to revisit the key problem-solving strategies that must show up in any new K–12 curriculum that purports to be bold, expansive, and disruptive:

- **Classify Information:** Sometimes simply identifying relevant and irrelevant information can create some clarity. Making a list or your own summary of the information could be beneficial.

- **Look for a Pattern:** One of the most historical strategies. Look for a pattern. It could be geometric, numerical, or algebraic. Just the search for a pattern is a critical element of thinking mathematically and fostering curiosity.

- **Draw a Diagram:** Students should always redraw a diagram in their own hand. It allows for a relaxed entry into the problem, perhaps stirring some insight just because of the movement of their pencils.

- **Estimate, Guess, and Check:** A direct method is not always readily available, so even an initial estimate of the mathematical situation has merit.
- **Work Backwards:** This is a critical strategy because it involves the student working in the complete opposite direction and sometimes uncovering ideas that might not have been seen with a straightforward approach.
- **Solve a Simpler Problem:** We have seen the power of this strategy a few times in this book. It is definitely one that will not only move the solution forward but often reveal some patterning underneath the problem in question. It anchors the student to the problem and reinforces the idea that sometimes seemingly complicated math problems can be solved by starting with "baby steps."
- **Check for Hidden Assumptions:** In some problems, the information concerning what is given is presented in a subtle manner that might not attract the attention of the student right away.
- **Introduce Something Extra:** Don't be afraid to add something to the situation—especially visually. Draw a new line. Extend lines. Rotate the picture. Maybe some symmetry will emerge that will make the problem easier to handle. Fold paper!
- **Make a Table, Chart, or Grid:** Just because the information is not presented in an organized form doesn't mean it can't be! Taking initiative and organizing it in some initial way will allow you to see something that might have been missed in the original presentation of the problem.
- **Walk away for a While:** This might seem like an odd strategy, but often taking a break from a problem and doing something else will relax the brain. Don't forget to take time out and enjoy

some of the nonmathematical joys in this life. [SMP: 1, 4, and at times all the others]

If you Google the words "math curriculum," you will get approximately a quarter of a billion results back. Page after page after page, you will find links to those words. Not surprisingly, because mathematics is a global subject, it never leaves the news cycle. Now add the word "fantasy." The results, although low, are very deceiving. There is only one result that yields all three words. The rest of the results involve the mathematics of fantasy sports. As you can see, the result has my (Sunil) name.

I find it shocking and dismaying that nobody else has dared to wildly dream about a "fantasy" math curriculum and commit that dream to ink. It makes you wonder not whether you are crazy, but just *how* crazy you are—to even contemplate the dismantling of mathematical institutions. What makes math education so impervious to imagining a complete reboot of the system? Is the whole system so daunting that we surrender to our comfort zones, carry conversations within safe radii of tradition, and continue to steadily march down the path most traveled?

Maybe the answers to those questions lie in the simple idea that the purpose of math education has never had a consensus. And its purpose has ranged from almost Victorian practicality to pure eudaimonia and human flourishing. Those are pretty wide goalposts. For the purposes of our book, Chris and I are pushing ideas that take mathematics to its highest virtues and loftiest ideals—that it is for the simple joy of it all!

Although we might be a generation or two away from a mathematical universe that looks markedly different from the one we live in, the revolution is afoot, and encouraging changes within our profession are happening with deeds and words. One of the exciting curriculum changes happening is in the state of New York and its *Next Generation Mathematics Learning Standards*, which were referenced in Chapter 1. It's a very hopeful vision of the widest possibilities and purposes of children learning mathematics. Much of this promise can be found in the "Glossary of Verbs" section. We have made it into a word cloud:

Interpret Compose
Know Demonstrate
Differentiate Use Specify
Calculate Evaluate
Describe Identify Express
ecompose Prove Justify Determine
Make Apply Compare Solve
Develop Explore Understand
Convert Derive Recognize
Write Reference State Analyze Fluent
Classify Verify Distingui

In that verb-rich cloud is one word that we would like to draw your attention to, especially in terms of laying the foundation of a new and broader vision for K–12 mathematics. That word is *explore*. The New York standards give this word the visionary power it deserves.

Explore	*Explore* requires the student to learn the concept in the standard through a variety of instructional activities. Repeated experiences with these concepts, with immersion in the concrete, are vital.
	Explore indicates that the topic is an important concept that builds the foundation for progression toward mastery in later grades. However, mastery at the current level is not expected for that standard.

Not expected. Brilliant. This simple statement yields the hope that sandbox learning in a rich and balanced environment of resources and approaches is not only possible but highly preferable. Play is being elevated more and more every day in mathematics as a serious part of a child's interaction with mathematics. We see mathematics as fun, and we could have a whole K–12 curriculum in which it is fun. As we have said explicitly and implicitly many times in this book, play and fun can and should be rigorous! The best word that elevates learning and play to that rigorous level is *explore*. Kids need to explore mathematics, and we, the math educators, have to *explore what they get to explore*. This is a tremendous but rewarding responsibility.

Another fellow math and music spirit, Matthew Oldridge, has given much thought to the reconstruction and reimagination of math education. We are sharing a screenshot of one of his articles below because we are in awe of the wonderfully humble and beautiful introduction:

There Exists An Elegant, Lovely, and Inspiring School Mathematics.

As a newcomer to the poetry and beauty of mathematics, but a dedicated learner, I have often been stunned into submission, struck dumb by its power. Learning mathematics is humbling. I know a tiny slice, and I am...

In the article, there is a powerful section in which he prefaces each statement with *There exists*, along with the symbol, ∃. There does exist such a school—in the imaginative and playful mind of Matthew Oldridge.

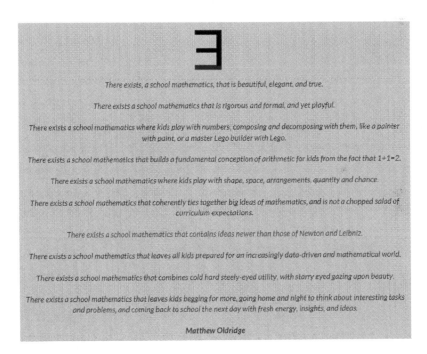

There exists, a school mathematics, that is beautiful, elegant, and true.

There exists a school mathematics that is rigorous and formal, and yet playful.

There exists a school mathematics where kids play with numbers, composing and decomposing with them, like a painter with paint, or a master Lego builder with Lego.

There exists a school mathematics that builds a fundamental conception of arithmetic for kids from the fact that 1+1=2.

There exists a school mathematics where kids play with shape, space, arrangements, quantity and chance.

There exists a school mathematics that coherently ties together big ideas of mathematics, and is not a chopped salad of curriculum expectations.

There exists a school mathematics that contains ideas newer than those of Newton and Leibniz.

There exists a school mathematics that leaves all kids prepared for an increasingly data-driven and mathematical world.

There exists a school mathematics that combines cold hard steely-eyed utility, with starry eyed gazing upon beauty.

There exists a school mathematics that leaves kids begging for more, going home and night to think about interesting tasks and problems, and coming back to school the next day with fresh energy, insights, and ideas.

Matthew Oldridge

The dreaming has begun. It is now time for the dreamers to come together. And they have.

In April 2016, I was at the Annual NCTM in lovely San Francisco. I met so many of my kindred math spirits for the first time. I not only met my inspiring coauthor, Chris, there, I also met James Tanton (who wrote the foreword for my first book) and Matthew Beyranevand (coeditor at *QED*). I also met Daniel Torres-Rangel. We all met for dinner one night. Eventually, Daniel and I had a chance to talk. A year later, through some social media back-and-forth, we decided to create a Google document.

Daniel Torres-Rangel has invited you to **edit** the following document:

▤ Fantasy K-12 Math Curriculum

`Open in Docs`

In the months to come, we invited math educators from all over the world to view the document and add to it. The response was overwhelming! Below are the main areas we organized in our document and the key points that were brought up in those parts. This is still very much a live document, so additions and edits will continue to happen. At this point, it is still a rich brainstorming session with organizational input and ideas continually framing its growth. Here's some of what that document contains:

Broad Goals

- Prioritize a deep, intrinsic love for mathematics over ability
- Reveal mathematics as a human enterprise with global traditions, accessible to all

- Advocate mathematics as a social experience with global connectedness
- Build strong bridges between arithmetic, algebra, and geometry
- Weave statistics/data interpretation as fundamental ideas for decoding information and articles on social media and analyzing duplicity found in predatory mathematics
- Enable all students, regardless of background, to be exposed to all the different ideas of mathematics and the host of college and university opportunities that are available

Characterization of the Learning

- Visible evidence of mathematics being learned through a rich glossary of verbs
- Play is at the foundation of this learning whenever possible
- Creating intellectual need and desire for algebra and geometry
- A balance between individual and group exploration
- Robust group discussions that value all insights and viewpoints
- Progressive assessment models that motivate students to demonstrate their ability and attitudes toward mathematics

Broad Domains

- Number theory
- Game theory
- Graph theory
- Decision-making mathematics involving statistics, probability, expectation, and utility
- Math history woven through all the domains
- Sacred geometry

- Daily inclusion of games, puzzles, conundrums, and brain-teasers
- Logic and proof/deductive reasoning problems
- Deeper focus on arithmetic
- Introduction of infinity at elementary levels with deeper explorations in middle and high school

Math Skills That Are Life Skills

- Proof
- Creativity
- Persistence
- Patience
- Estimation/reasonableness
- Resilience
- Risk-taking
- Courage
- Communication and collaboration
- Discipline and rigor

Math Concepts That Need Introduction/Rejuvenation

- Topology
- Exploding Dots
- Fractals
- Egyptian Fractions

Questions to Ask Ourselves

- How much of this already exists? Will it be more curation or creation?
- How should we build this and where should we start first?
- Can we agree on essential goals and objectives at this point?

- Where should we look for partnership to begin implementation?
- Where does homework fit into this model?
- Do we have to change the idea of what homework looks like?
- What other categories do we need to consider?

HAPPINESS IS NOT AN IDEAL OF REASON, BUT OF IMAGINATION

IMMANUEL KANT

Back in May 2015, I gave my first Ignite talk at OAME, the Annual Meeting for Ontario Math Educators. It is a challenge to create twenty slides that automatically fast forward every fifteen seconds, all the while trying to maintain a seamless five-minute talk. The title of my Ignite was, "Mathematics: A Right to Beauty."

Ignite OAME 2015, Sunil Singh
bit.do/mathrecess11

The initial slides pay homage to Willy Wonka, and the first words I utter to a math audience of more than three hundred people are, "Close your eyes. Make a wish. Count to three. Come with me."

Chris and I would like you to come with us! Come with us on a mathematical journey and adventure into the unknown where every new idea is given a place of incubation—much like how new and innovative startups are provided with a creative environment to sprout and thrive.

Here we will begin building the natural bridge that will carry us into our final chapter. The link between our humanity and our amazing ability to imagine completely new and revolutionary ideas. In the summer of 2018, I took the initiative to contact Berkeley Everett, who at the time was a first-grade teacher in New York. His tweets about mathematics were intriguing. We were following each other and commenting quite a bit through the limited domain of Twitter texts.

In our one-hour conversation, which unintentionally flowed in and out of making mathematics a most human endeavor, Everett said something I had never considered in teaching mathematics. Ever! I have brushed up against what he said with the ideas that we should inspire students with math instead of trying to make them *good* at math. Everett took it well beyond that. He said our society turns every hobby, pastime, and interest into a competition and full-blown immersion for the purposes of full-blown mastery. Collectively, we asked, "Why does everything, including math, produce so much demand to be an expert?" I felt my heart beating a little bit faster, almost anticipating a new idea to add to my treasure chest of imagination.

Everett then elaborated and introduced *that* word. Why can't people just dabble in mathematics? *Dabble.* It even has a fun sound. Isn't this just exploration without some of the pedagogical weight? Imagine the pressure lifted from kids' shoulders if we allowed them to simply dabble. Berkeley often plays with numbers and shares his explorations on social media. He is a kid at heart—mathematical heart—whose dabblings embody the spirit of mathematical recess for all!

Berkeley Everett @BerkeleyEverett · Feb 11
I was "tinkering" with a pattern I noticed... what do YOU notice? What does this make you wonder? #noticewonder #mtbos #iteachmath @Mathgarden

Number	How to Make It
2	1 and 1
3	1 and 2
4	1 and 3, 2 and 2
5	1 and 4, 2 and 3
6	1 and 5, 2 and 4, 3 and 3
7	1 and 6, 2 and 5, 3 and 4
8	1 and 7, 2 and 6, 3 and 5, 4 and 4
9	1 and 8, 2 and 7, 3 and 6, 4 and 5
10	1 and 9, 2 and 8, 3 and 7, 4 and 6, 5 and 5
11	1 and 10, 2 and 9, 3 and 8, 4 and 7, 5 and 6

If you noticed in the above post, Berkeley used the word *tinkering* instead of the word *dabble* that he had shared with me. That is because he was giving a supportive wink to the person who responded to Berkeley's introduction of the word *dabble* into the lexicon of math recess kind of verbs. That person would be David Petro, a math leader in my home province of Ontario. A math leader from the United States and a math leader from Canada. Both evoking the themes of rich play with words that are reflective of light-hearted curiosity. *The times they are a changin'*—finally.

Playful Verbs In Learning Mathematics

"Dabble"

Berkeley Everett
K-5 Math Specialist, California

"Tinker"

David Petro
OAME President, Ontario

Everett's background is as a classical/jazz pianist. That's right; like me, he doesn't come from a math background. He brings to the study, however, the much-needed qualities of *curiosity* and *vulnerability*. If these are not two of the highest qualities to be human, then I am not sure what is. Math education will never reform itself without these allusions of humanness.

Although it was only the first time we had connected through voice, the mathematics that we discussed—through a lens I had never really used—quickly cemented another friendship. Berkeley Everett is now a K–5 math specialist in his hometown of Los Angeles. His path to his current position is inspiring for all of us. The growth mindset applies not only to students but to teachers as well. We don't have to be experts. We don't have to be the answer key. What we have to be is honest and passionate. Those are not only desirable qualities in a math teacher. Turns out they are desirable qualities in friendship.

QUESTIONS FOR DEEPER DISCUSSION

1. What are the purposes of a curriculum in mathematics?

2. Which of the aspects of the Fantasy Math Curriculum appeal to you most and why?

3. What are your thoughts on "dabbling" in mathematics? How can you encourage your students to venture out into this world?

CHAPTER 10

Why Can't We Be Friends?

*Each friend represents a world in us, a world
not born until they arrive, and it is only by
this meeting that a new world is born.*

—Anaïs Nin

There always has to be an end to any book. There always has to be some kind of wrapping up of ideas. We have chosen to leave you with the most critical idea of learning mathematics in today's and tomorrow's classrooms. Mathematics is harnessing the social energy in this age of disruption, and as such, critical shifts are beginning to happen in how we see the broadest and loftiest aspirations of learning mathematics.

The Global Math Project is uniting millions of students with different backgrounds, customs, and beliefs every year with uplifting mathematics. Francis Su's idea that mathematics is for human flourishing has become a revolutionary call. Equity in learning mathematics has become a vessel to hear compelling stories about inclusion and belonging. Mathematics is now widely appreciated and taught through powerful verbs such as *play* and *explore*. A complete redistribution of trust from a vertical, hierarchical structure to a horizontal, democratized one is now the new roadmap for humans interacting and sharing in the twenty-first century.

Like swirling gases that are precursors to the birth of a new solar system, these game-changing ideas are beginning to contract into a new solar system for math education. Unbounded by determination and creativity, the endgame for teaching and learning mathematics is an organic fusion of all of the elements in the paragraph above. Mathematics is coming home, and so are we. We have created mathematics to connect all of us, and to be explored as a social experience to bring us closer together socially and emotionally.

In 2017, I was an invited speaker at NCTM in Washington. They even gave me my own ballroom to make my presentation! As you can see by the title below, my workshop was an amalgam of the emergent ideas in math education. The new social endpoints can be defined now. Connection and friendship are where mathematics will lead us.

142 ISSUES
The Socialization Power of Mathematics and the Higher Purpose of Collaboration in the Digital Age
General Interest Session

The maturation of social media and the emergent currency of trust among strangers is now reshaping the landscape of how and why we are teaching and sharing mathematics. The depth and richness of mathematical discussions are creating equally powerful human connections that are serving as new social endpoints for mathematics in the 21st century.

Sunil Singh
🐦 @Mathgarden
Scolab, Montreal, Quebec, Canada
Walter E. Washington Convention Center, Ballroom A

Everything has been flipped 180 degrees because of this new socialization soil that is allowing all these great ideas to grow. In the past, it might have been something like learning facilitates friendship. Now? Friendship, being the goal, facilitates learning. We share our resources and ideas about mathematics so that we can simply share ourselves. It is all becoming thankfully blurred, and mathematics has traded in some of its traditional stiffness and anachronisms for ideas that go deeper in learning not just about mathematics, but perhaps, and more importantly, about each other and ourselves.

Anthony Bourdain

It would be remiss of us not to weave in the lasting impressions of the late and wonderfully humble Anthony Bourdain. I met him at a book signing in 2005, when he was already popular thanks to his *Cook's Tour* and *No Reservations* shows. When it was my turn to get my book signed, it was I, not he, that hurried things along. The wisdom that Bourdain showered the world with is strikingly in sync with what mathematics has become and will become in the coming years—a human passion, like food, to connect people of every race, color, and class. The world humbled Bourdain. The world of mathematics offers much the same. The more we travel through it—*want to travel through it*—the more we realize how little we know. How life's beauty is a strange cocktail of too little time and too many things to experience. The passage below by Bourdain drips with all that…

> It seems that the more places I see and experience, the bigger I realize the world to be. The more I become aware of, the more I realize how relatively little I know of it, how many places I have still to go, how much more there is to learn. Maybe that's enlightenment

enough—to know that there is no final resting place of the mind, no moment of smug clarity. Perhaps wisdom, at least for me, means realizing how small I am, and unwise, and how far I have yet to go.

This is exactly how Chris and I see mathematics. Bourdain's shows in the beginning focused on the food. Toward the end of CNN's *Parts Unknown*, the food became a medium to understand and get to know everyday people. Mathematics is now serving the exact same purpose. The quality of the mathematics that we share becomes the quality of the connection—to potentially deeper bonds of friendship. Imagine sitting on the porch and weaving the mind-boggling immensity of something like Graham's Number while staring at the sky. If you are sharing this moment, then it is not just mathematics we have to thank, but more specifically, the softer lens we are seeing it through.

When Sunil and I first started talking about this book, one of the ideas that we played with was giving to you some mathematics appropriate for the beach, BBQ, bar, and backyard. We wanted to share ideas you could work with socially, at your leisure, for pleasant company and joyful times. That was one of the first titles we considered to be honest: *Mathematics for the Beach, Brunch, or Bar*. Here's a mockup of a playful cover we developed.

MATHEMATICS FOR
THE BEACH, BRUNCH
AND BAR

CONNECTING PASSIONATE PEOPLE WITH LIFE'S
PLEASURES THROUGH NUMBERS

Chris Brownell and Sunil Singh

We wanted to share with you the real possibility of connecting with others through the medium of mathematical thought.

Looking over my social media posts on Twitter and Facebook, I can see that in the beginning the discussions were on mathematics. Now, for many of my online connections, they are about kids, recipes, travel, politics, and the mutual desire to meet in person.

In Math We Trust

It's not just math we trust. Because we are intertwined with math we, as social and emotional humans, trust. We might not be fully aware of how strong this trust is, but just see the powerful connections we make and attribute to finding kindred spirits who share similar ideas and philosophy about teaching mathematics.

This idea about trust in mathematics is not an opinion or even some visceral reaction. It is simply just the mechanics of how humans are channeling ideas about trust. Rachel Botsman is the world-renowned expert on the shifting trends that have been happening the last ten years in the world. There are dozens of videos on YouTube that speak to the wisdom of trust that is affecting things consciously and subconsciously in math education. But this short two-minute video captures so many of the symbolic changes happening—and so many of the symbolic changes that are still needed.

Rachel Botsman, "Who Can You Trust?"
bit.do/mathrecess12

Trust is like energy — it doesn't get destroyed, it changes form. For a long time in history, trust has flowed upwards towards the CEOs, towards experts, academics, economists, and regulators. Now that's being inverted — trust is now flowing sideways, between individuals, 'friends,' peers and strangers. There's plenty of trust out there, it's just flowing to different people and places

~Rachel Botsman 2017~

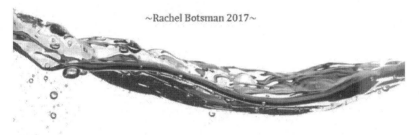

Disruption in math education is occurring because of leaps of trust between thousands of math educators online and offline every day. This leap is leading to robust discussions and actions from all connected partners in math education—students, parents, administrators, coaches, and the ones who anchor it all, classroom teachers. Disruption and innovation have become issues of our heart. Elizabeth Bostwick's book is passionate call for just that. Our leap must be together to make the necessary changes.

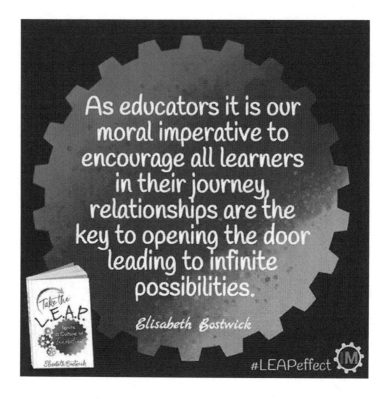

As educators it is our moral imperative to encourage all learners in their journey, relationships are the key to opening the door leading to infinite possibilities.

Elisabeth Bostwick

#LEAPeffect

Just as every single institution is undergoing a complete transformation of its purpose—*to remain purposeful*—math education is also using the redistribution of trust to guide its "*re's*", which we emphasized in our introduction. They have been wonderfully enhanced here by @lilmathgirl, a person both Chris and I follow on Twitter, who challenges us—and everyone—to dig deeper into revolutionary thoughts of our time. Her Twitter banner, *in graffiti font*, reads "We Play Math."

Disruption Begins With "Re"

Rewire

Rewrite

Redirect

Re-teach

Redesign

Rethink

Reimagine

@lilmathgirl

We are all discussing. Constantly. What used to be ripples of conversation have turned into full-blown waves of the "re" ideas crashing against the shores of traditional ideas of learning and teaching mathematics. We are doing this because we know that schools no longer work in creating the autonomous and feisty learners that we all desire. And none of this would have been possible if there had not been the global trust shift in this last generation—which has led to more global connectedness and curiosity for rebuilding a curriculum that goes even beyond *pure imagination.*

In Spring of 2017 at NCSM in Washington, a confluence of so many elements we have touched on in this book came together. The talented Jill Gough (@jgough), from Atlanta, Georgia, came to my workshop—as both a kindred math spirit *and a friend*—and put together one of her famous Sketchnotes. It was all organically braided by trust and friendship.

227

Twenty years ago, we cautioned our neighbors from using their credit cards on the internet. Now we don't even blink about letting strangers into our homes (Airbnb) or hopping into a car with one (Uber). Mathematics doesn't sit in a vacuum, even though some of us have unintentionally allowed it to do so. Mathematics gets pollinated by revolutionary ideas just like any other aspect of our society. We just need to be more cognizant of the changes to embrace the changes, to desire to relearn. The alternative, as forecasted by Alvin Toffler in his 1970 book *Future Shock*, spoke to an isolation that has become a sad reality in many parts of our society.

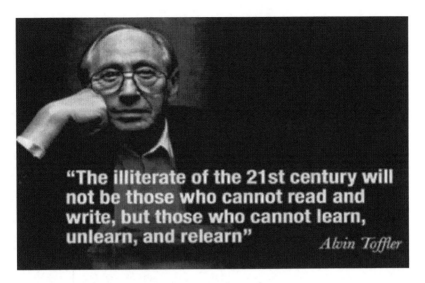

"The illiterate of the 21st century will not be those who cannot read and write, but those who cannot learn, unlearn, and relearn" *Alvin Toffler*

The confidence and trust to collaborate with each other in math education has never been more pronounced. Our cups are over-flowing with them. So much so that we are reframing mathematics through ideas of socialization and connection. There is no option but to build friendships near and far. And as such, we are left with only one option that encompasses all of this...

Humanity or Bust

All the micro- and macroideas of mathematics lie in wait for all of us to explore and share. And, as has been hopefully and thematically communicated in this book, it is an endeavor that is warm, amiable, and addictively charming. Mathematics has been, above all things, a most human endeavor. As our planet deals with situations and problems that often eclipse the urgency of teaching mathematics, it is even more incumbent on all of us to ensure that mathematics—harnessing the winds of disruption and trust shifts—illuminates an even stronger light of humanness. We cannot get pulled back into outdated models of efficiency. Even the word *success* is a limiting word as to the potential of what mathematics can mean in the lives of all our students.

We must go beyond everything that we have ever done. We must meet each other with openness and vulnerability and not be fearful of change but excited by it. Not be bogged down in the administrative burdens, but instead, challenge them. It is not enough to merely reveal mathematics for its truth; it must also reveal the truth about us. This will of course occur in quiet times with our own personal reflections, but a vast majority of our math adventures—hopefully transcending—will be with each other. And, at bottom, our collective and coordinated efforts to rehumanize math education is rooted in not failing our kids and in maintaining a lifetime passion for mathematics. The staggering breadth and depth of mathematics is there for the taking. Students need our guidance and trust to nurture this curiosity.

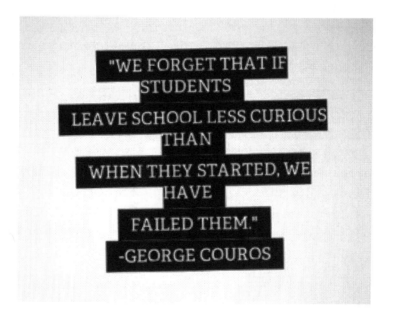

The benefits of teaching and learning mathematics through a wider social domain has a calling that goes beyond the connecting powers of friendship. For the first time in the history of math education, the idea of humanity as the goal for math education can be seen. Sure, it is still in its infancy, but that is why we wrote this book. Playing with math. Playing with each other. Creating new worlds inside of us that are inseparable combinations with the people we befriend and the quality of the mathematics we share. Our time is up. The bell for this recess to be over is about to ring. There will be others. Many, many others. Although we believe that the ideas in this book have been bountiful, we hope that the inspiration to find your own has been even greater. Disruption is a force. In physics, that equals mass multiplied by acceleration. The acceleration is increasing, and so is the mass of our ideas.

If we teach and learn with our hearts, then creating a curriculum that is joyful and creative will come sooner than later. In one of my conversations with Maria Droujkova, whom I mentioned a few chapters back, she was curious as to what "kind mathematics" would look like. A year later, at the end of 2018, in a strange coincidence, or perhaps not, Steve Khan (University of Alberta) and Alayne Armstrong (University of Regina) put out a call for submissions regarding this.

Call for Submissions: Math-a-POLKA: Mathematics—A Place Of Loving Kindness And . . .

Title of Special Issue: Math-a-POLKA: Mathematics—A Place Of Loving Kindness And . . .

Guest Editors: Steven Khan (University of Alberta) & Alayne Armstrong (University of Regina)

Twentieth century frameworks about the teaching, learning, knowing and doing of mathematics are giving way to emerging sensibilities seeded by a re-invigorated emphasis on human(e) values, grounded in intentional and explicit practices of mindfully curating attention (Acosta & Adamson, 2017), awareness and action with loving kindness. This mythopoetic work (Macdonald, 1981/1995) is emerging from the amplification of activities among popularizers, proselytizers and policy-makers, enabled by networked technology. One node, for example, is the invitation to re-imagine mathematics education as being for "flourishing" (Su, 2017).

This bold idea of rethinking mathematics through the softest and sometimes most fragile lens, our hearts, is a testament that we have set the dials for math education toward the simplest and most complex resting place—our own humanity. It demands a wider search for the possibilities for learning mathematics. But that search for a new frontier of math pedagogy begins with us and with each other. Our values go beyond the narrow domain of functionality and performance. They are of the heart, which means they are boundless. Kindness is a worthy destination in itself. Pair that up with mathematics, and all of a sudden we are transported to a world *of pure imagination.*

Where is the math pedagogy that instructs us to teach with empathy, grace, humility, doubt, confusion, space, time, play, doodling, daydreaming, awe, wonder, weirdness, fantasy, reverence, leisure, connection, community, justice, freedom, humanity, hope, and love...?

Our mindsets must be firmly set on this dial of disruption. There is a vast universe of mathematics to explore. Let's spend as much time as possible exploring it together, forging friendships along the way. The worlds of mathematics and friendship are the best gifts we can give our students and ourselves. Luckily, they come interlaced now.

The promise of friendship ensures that the environment in which we continue to nurture the culture of rich mathematical thinking is wholly supportive and inspiring. Although we have left you with, hopefully, lots of math, *any subsequent sequels will be written by you*— regardless of your background in mathematics. Chris and I have just shared a mere fraction of what is available and accessible, even though our book was written to be content rich! Please take the problems and ideas that have fascinated you and bundle them up with the stories of Marjorie Rice and Berkeley Everett. Continue your mathematical adventures. Create your own mathematical identity that is unique to you.

If we have crafted our book with enough creativity and humanity, then perhaps we have inspired you to embark on these journeys and share them with feral abandon. As such, this book is merely a prologue to the playful future of math education. A future of all our disruptive stories, braided together, to stay together. We hope to hear from you.

QUESTIONS FOR DEEPER DISCUSSION

1. Before this book, would you have considered mathematics a social endeavor? How is that perception different now?

2. Do you feel that the math conferences you have attended helped cultivate deeper connections with fellow math educators? What would you change about the math conferences you attend to make that happen?

3. What would a "kind mathematics" look like in your classroom? What could you do to move toward that goal tomorrow or next week or next month?

NOTES

Introduction

Araujo, Antonio. Facebook Post. December 3, 2018. bit.ly/2N5icq6.

Byers, Williams. *How Mathematicians Think: Using Ambiguity, Contradiction, and Paradox to Create Mathematics.* Princeton: Princeton University Press, 2007.

Hoffman, Jan. "Square Root of Kids' Math Anxiety: Their Parents' Help." *The New York Times* (New York) Aug. 24, 2015.

Lockhart, Paul. *A Mathematician's Lament: How School Cheats Us Out of Our Most Fascinating and Imaginative Art Form.* New York: Bellevue Literary Press, 2009.

Resnick, Mitchel. *Lifelong Kindergarten: Cultivating Creativity through Projects, Passion, Peers, and Play.* Cambridge: The MIT Press, 2017.

Singh, Sunil. *Pi of Life: The Hidden Happiness of Mathematics.* Lanham: Rowman & Littlefield, 2017.

—. "The Road to Learning Mathematics Goes through Struggle, Not Efficiency." *Medium* article, October 1, 2018. bit.ly/2SVXOwS.

Williams, Thomas J. Twitter Post. December 9, 2018. bit.ly/2tpsDvv.

Willy Wonka & The Chocolate Factory. Directed by Mel Stuart. 1971. Burbank, CA: Warner Brothers. 2001. DVD.

Added Introduction for Teachers and School Administrators in the USA

Common Core State Standards in Math (2010): bit.ly/2SPdimA.

Chapter 1

Jo Boaler Presentation, October 6, 2018. Global Math Symposium. San Jose, CA.

Ginsburg, K. R. "The Importance of Play in Promoting Healthy Child Development and Maintaining Strong Parent-Child Bonds." *Pediatrics* 119, no. 1 (2007): 182-91. doi:10.1542/peds.2006-2697.

Lockhart, Paul, content about Sprouts (the Simplicio/Salviati dialogue). *A Mathematician's Lament*. New York: Bellevue Literary Press, 2009.

ibid.

Meyer, Dan. "Math Class Needs a Makeover." Filmed March 2010 in New York. TED Video. 11:32, ted.com/talks/dan_meyer_math_curriculum_makeover?language=en.

Meyer, Dan. Twitter Post. Jan. 5, 2018. bit.ly/2IdPLaD.

Next Generation Learning Standards for the State of New York. nysed.gov/next-generation-learning-standards.

"Recreational Math: Game of Sprouts." Posted July 9, 2012. YouTube video. 2:38, youtube.com/watch?v=XXhS8PiUTvM.

Singh, Sunil. Twitter Post. March 2, 2018. bit.ly/2UQUUqC.

Su, Francis. Speech at Joint Mathematics Meeting, Mathematical Association of America, January 2017.

Tanton, James. Exploding Dots, December 2018. explodingdots.org.

Won't You Be My Neighbor. Directed by Morgan Neville. 2018. Universal City, CA: Universal Studios Home Entertainment, 2018. DVD.

Chapter 2

Boaler Jo. The Sketchnote image, Twitter, July 2018. bit.ly/2TMRogQ.

Graphic on Mihaly Csikszentmihalyi's Flow concept. In: Csikszentmihalyi, Mihaly. *Flow: The Psychology of Optimal Experience*. New York: Harper Row, 2009.

Finkel, Dan. "Five Principles of Extraordinary Math Teaching." Filmed February 2016. TEDx Talk, 14:41. youtube.com/watch?v=ytVneQUA5-c.

"The Josephus Problem - Numberphile." YouTube video, 13:57. Posted October 28, 2016. youtube.com/watch?v=uCsD3ZGzMgE&feature=youtu.be.

Lahey, Jessica. "Recess Without Rules." *The Atlantic,* January 2014.

Rowinsky, Nico. Twitter Post. September. 5, 2018. bit.ly/2TOoo8r.

Scolab (2017). "Exploding Dots." explodingdots.org. Accessed February 14, 2019.

Singh, Sunil. NYT Numberplay column, August 2016. nyti.ms/2Ebmyta.

—. Twitter Post. September 3, 2018. bit.ly/2DFzoyh.

Waddell, Glenn, Jr. Tweet images regarding the 24 Problem, September 5, 2018. bit.ly/2WZEKg.

Chapter 3

Beyranevand, Matthew (2017). "Retaking Assessments: Many math teachers are late to the party!" *Medium.com.* bit.ly/2GpuEQZ . Accessed February 14, 2019.

Cuoco, Al, Goldenberg, E. Paul, and June Mark. "Habits of Mind: An Organizing Principle for Mathematics Curricula." *Journal of Mathematical Behavior*. 15 vol. 4 (1996): 375-402.

Lennon, John. "Imagine." *JohnLennon.com*. February 5, 2019. johnlennon.com/music/albums/imagine/.

Martin, Dave. "How I abolished grading." October 2017. bit. ly/2S1DRQT. Accessed February 14, 2019.

—. "No percentage marks from Red Deer maths teacher." bit. ly/2BA9JXB. Accessed February 14, 2019.

Ravitch, Diane. "The Working Notes for My Speech at Oberlin Conference on the State of American Democracy. *DianeRavitch. net*. November 19, 2017. dianeravitch.net/2017/11/19/the-working-notes-for-my-speech-at-oberlin-conference-on-the-state-of-american-democracy.

Schneider, Jack, and Ethan Hutt. "Making the grade: a history of the A–F marking scheme," *Journal of Curriculum Studies* 46, vol. 2 (2014) 201-224.

Wolfram, Conrad. "Teaching Kids Real Math with Computers." Filmed July 2010. TED Talk, 17:12. ted.com/talks/conrad_wolfram_teaching_kids_real_math_with_computers?language=en.

Chapter 4

Abbott, Robert. Logic Mazes. logicmazes.com.

Cows in the Classroom, bovine math puzzle. bovinemath.com.

Kass, Sam. Rock, Paper, Scissors puzzle. November 2008. samkass.com/theories/RPSSL.html.

"Let 'Em Roll" *Plus Magazine*. December 10, 2006. plus.maths.org/content/let-em-roll.

NYT Numberplay blog, Tax collector puzzle. nyti.ms/2N8mEUU.

"Ontario Place—Children's Village." youtu.be/jJpmk7QOq30. Accessed February 5, 2019.

Pearse, Margie. Twitter Math Peeps tweet. bit.ly/1ChTjfl.

Chapter 5

Moore, Michael (2017). "A Documentary on Finnish Schools." bit.ly/2SOweBT. Accessed February 14, 2019.

Sahlberg, Pasi. *Finnish Lesson 2.0: What Can the World Learn from Educational Change in Finland*. New York: Teachers College Press, 2015.

Chapter 6

Euclid's Elements have been translated, printed, re-printed and exist in the public domain in a wide variety of versions, Chris' favorite version is maintained online by a professor, David Joyce, at Clark University. They use Javascripts to allow you to manipulate geometric objects and visualize what is happening. They can be found at this shortened link: bit.ly/2S35Qzv. Accessed February 14, 2019.

Gardner, M. On tessellating the plane with convex polygon tiles. *Scientific American* (July 1975), pp. 112–117. Also Chapter 13 in *Time Travel and Other Mathematical Bewilderments*. New York: W.H. Freeman, 1988; pp. 163-176.

Mubeen, Junaid. Social Media post about math, January 8, 2017. bit.ly/2GJCJ2i.

Saccheri, G. (1697). *"Euclid cleared of every flaw."* N.p., Public domain.

Schattschneider, Doris (2018). "Marjorie Rice and the MAA tiling." *Journal of Mathematics and the Arts* 12:2-3:114-127; doi: 10.1080/17513472.2018.1453740.

The Imitation Game. Directed by Morten Tyldum. 2014. New York: The Weinstein Company, 2015. DVD.

The story told of James Tanton's development of Exploding Dots is culled from many conversations between the three of us, James, Chris, and Sunil. Direct quotes were pulled from a correspondence Chris and James conducted via email in October 2018 immediately following the Second Annual Global Math Week. Used with his permission.

Chapter 7

Finkel, Dan. "Can You Solve the Time Travel Riddle?" Filmed 2018. YouTube video, 4:31. youtube.com/watch?v=ukUPojrPFPA.

Five Guys. "Prime Spirals." *Medium* article, December 20, 2016. medium.com/five-guys-facts/12-19-16-lefko-d473c0687fcb.

Numberphile (2016). "The Seven Bridges of Königsberg."bit.ly/2BvXN9d. Accessed February 14, 2019.

Singh, Sunil. Twitter post. August 19, 2018. bit.ly/2Gr4BsC.

Chapter 8

Carroll, Lewis. *Alice's Adventures in Wonderland*, London: MacMillan Publishers, 1865.

Numberphile, (2014). "Fool-proof method for finding primes." bit.ly/2X3Usaz Accessed February 14, 2019.

Numberphile (2018). "The Golden Ratio (why it is so irrational)." bit.ly/2SRYFPc Accessed February 14, 2019.

Chapter 9

Brownell, Chris. "Mathematical Fluency: What does it Mean, Why is it Important?" *AIMS Center for Math and Science Education* podcast, Episode 29, March 30, 2017. aimsedu.

org/2017/03/30/episode-29-mathematical-fluency-what-does-it-mean-why-is-it-important/?highlight=fluency.

Mubeen, Junaid. "Everyone in Your School Could Be a Maths Genius." YouTube video, 22:15. December 9, 2016. bit.ly/2tnlLPB.

Oldridge, Matthew. "There Exists An Elegant, Lovely, and Inspiring School Mathematics," *QED, Medium.com*. October 17, 2017. medium.com/q-e-d/there-exists-an-elegant-lovely-and-inspiring-school-mathematics-4a25f31b597a. O'Shaughnessey, Arthur. Music and Moonlight. N.p.: 1873.

O'Shaughnessey, Arthur. Music and Moonlight. N.p.: 1873.

Singh, Sunil. "Mathematics: A Right to Beauty." YouTube video, 5:03. July 23, 2015. Available at: bit.ly/2SQZrfq.

Willy Wonka & The Chocolate Factory. Directed by Mel Stuart. 1971. Burbank, CA: Warner Brothers. 2001. DVD.

Chapter 10

Botsman, Rachel. "Who You Can Trust?" YouTube video, 2:38. July 17, 2017. bit.ly/2GHLudf.

Bourdain, Anthony. *No Reservations*. "Peru." Travel Channel, April 10, 2006.

Gough, Jill. Sketchnote image, Social Media, Global Connectedness and the Collapse of Trust Institutions NCSM 2017, Washington, DC.

Toffler, Alvin. *Future Shock*. New York: Random House, 1970.

More Books from
IM͙PRESS

Empower
What Happens When Students Own Their Learning
By A.J. Juliani and John Spencer

In an ever-changing world, educators and parents must take a role in helping students prepare themselves for *anything*. That means unleashing their creative potential! In *Empower*, A.J. Juliani and John Spencer provide teachers, coaches, and administrators with a roadmap that will inspire innovation, authentic learning experiences, and practical ways to empower students to pursue their passions while in school.

Learner-Centered Innovation
Spark Curiosity, Ignite Passion, and Unleash Genius
By Katie Martin

Learning opportunities and teaching methods must evolve to match the ever-changing needs of today's learners. In *Learner-Centered Innovation*, Katie Martin offers insights into how to make the necessary shifts and create an environment where learners at every level are empowered to take risks in pursuit of learning and growth rather than perfection.

Unleash Talent
Bringing Out the Best in Yourself and the Learners You Serve
By Kara Knollmeyer

In *Unleash Talent*, educator and principal Kara Knollmeyer explains that by exploring the core elements of talent—passion, skills, and personality traits—you can uncover your gifts and help others do the same. Whether you are a teacher, administrator, or custodian, this insightful guide will empower you to use your unique talents to make a powerful impact on your school community.

Reclaiming Our Calling
Hold on to the Heart, Mind, and Hope of Education
By Brad Gustafson

Children are more than numbers, and we are called to teach and reach them accordingly. In this genre-busting book, award-winning educator and principal Brad Gustafson uses stories to capture the heart, mind, and hope of education.

Take the L.E.A.P.
Ignite a Culture of Innovation
By Elizabeth Bostwick

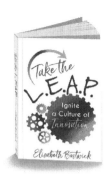

Take the L.E.A.P.: Ignite a Culture of Innovation will inspire and support you as you to take steps to grow beyond traditional and self-imposed boundaries. Award-winning educator Elisabeth Bostwick shares stories and practical strategies to help you challenge conventional thinking and create the conditions that empower meaningful learning.

Drawn to Teach
An Illustrated Guide to Transforming Your Teaching
Written by Josh Stumpenhorst, Illustrated by Trevor Guthke

If you're looking for ways to help your students succeed, you won't find the answer in gimmicks, trends, or fads. Great teaching isn't about test results or data; it's about connecting with students and empowering them to own their learning. Through this clever, illustrated guide, Josh Stumpenhorst reveals the key characteristics all top educators share in common and shows you how to implement them in your teaching practice.

About the Authors

Sunil Singh was a high school math and physics teacher for nineteen years. He has taught every grade level, and in every situation imaginable, from the socio-economic challenges of tough, urban schools in Toronto, Ontario, to an International Baccalaureate School in Switzerland. His views on the purpose and potential for learning mathematics—and that all students are capable of loving mathematics—have been strongly reinforced in this wide domain of experiences.

Sunil has viewed mathematics as an adventure his entire life, and now mathematics is providing adventures for him in writing and traveling. He has given more than fifty presentations on creative mathematics across North America, including The Royal Conservatory of Mathematics in Toronto and The Museum of Mathematics in New York. His interactive Family Math Nights have taken him as far as Austin, Texas. He is the author of *Pi of Life: The Hidden Happiness of Mathematics* and was a regular writer for the *New York Times* Numberplay section. He is also a co-editor at *Q.E.D.,* a popular blog for "disruptive" math writing. He has been a featured speaker at math conferences such as NCTM and NCSM.

Although he was a high school math teacher for most of his career, Sunil's focus now is K–8 mathematics, a devotion completely inspired by visiting his daughter's grade 1 class in 2014, and witnessing the enormous capabilities of the youngest students in mathematics. In addition to mathematics, his passions include music, cooking, baking, traveling, soccer, hockey, dogs, craft beer, and his two kids, Aidan and Raya.

Christopher S. Brownell, PhD, is a husband, father of three grown daughters, and a 14-year veteran high school math teacher turned university math and math education professor, now with 19 years' experience at that level. His main professional focus for the past two decades has been in supporting teachers of mathematics at every phase of their career. This includes  teaching both undergraduate mathematics majors and in-service teachers at Fresno Pacific and Claremont Graduate Universities.

His lessons, talks, and presentations seek to communicate that mathematics is a fundamental human characteristic, something we all have within us, something with a great story to be told. Convinced that knowing mathematics will make anyone better at whatever they choose or find themselves doing in their professional lives, he is involved in several organizations that share these goals. Among them is the Global Math Project, for which he is an ambassador, the Experience Workshop, an international collective of educators working and researching in the area of STEAM education, the National Council of Teachers of Mathematics, and the Mathematical

Association of America. Recently he was elected as a fellow of the International Society for Design and Development in Education.

His work as a professor has recently taken him to several European countries and South Korea, where he has spoken at conferences and gatherings of societies dedicated to mathematical art, STEAM education, and the use of digital tools in teaching mathematics. To Chris mathematics is as creative an endeavor as storytelling, art, play-writing, and music making—the doing of which brings him great joy.

Made in the USA
Lexington, KY
16 June 2019